Preface

GUIDE ON ENVIRONMENTAL STATEMENTS FOR PLANNING PROJECTS THAT REQUIRE ENVIRONMENTAL ASSESSMENT

Environmental assessment seeks to ensure that significant environmental effects are fully taken into account in development decisions. Establishing, presenting and considering environmental information in a systematic way assists all parties with an interest in environmental assessment - developers, the decision making authority, consultees and the general public. For this reason the quality of environmental statements has been shown to be crucial to the success of the environmental assessment process.

This Good Practice Guide distils the best experience of the past 8 years. We consulted widely on a draft of the guidance and I am grateful to the many of you who contributed ideas and specific suggestions. I hope the guide will ensure the easier and speedier consideration of development projects which require environmental assessment. But this is just a means to an end which I am keen to promote - a high quality environment in this country.

Robert Jones

Minister of State, Department of the Environment

CONTENTS

TABLES

FIGURES

INTRODUCTION

1. This Guide is intended primarily for developers and their advisers who propose projects which they have already agreed, or which the planning authority has directed, require Environmental Assessment (EA). Its aim is to help them prepare good quality, objective Environmental Statements (ES) which, in turn, should help to speed and smooth the planning decision making process.

2. Although the requirement for an ES may at first sight seem an unwelcome complication to the planning process, the procedures associated with undertaking EA are concerned with establishing good practice. In many cases they simply bring forward to an earlier stage work which would have to be undertaken by the developer in any case. EA also has benefits for everyone involved in the process by making available at an early stage clear, factual, well presented information about the effects a proposed development is likely to have on the environment, and the measures proposed to reduce or compensate for those effects.

3. Preparing the ES in parallel with project design offers the **developer** a framework within which project design and environmental considerations can interact; it helps **planning authorities and environmental authorities** with information which should form a basis for better decision making; and for the **public and community groups** most likely to be concerned with the proposed development, it will help allay fears often created by a lack of information about the effects of the proposed development.

4. In the UK, environmental assessment may be required under a number of different legislative and regulatory regimes, for example trunk roads under the Highways Act 1980. This guide is concerned only with those projects covered by Town and Country Planning legislation. However, the basic principles have a wider significance and are equally relevant to projects requiring environmental assessment under other legislation.

5. **Part I** of the guide sets out an advisory framework for the environmental assessment by the developer; **Part II** provides a framework for the preparation of the Environmental Statement.

6. The guide also contains **Appendices** on a number of environmental topics which may be of relevance to a project requiring EA and which may need to be dealt with in the ES. Developers and their specialist advisers can refer to these if they are appropriate. However, in doing so they should bear in mind that the information given is purely illustrative of the range and type of information which may be covered in an environmental statement. It is not a definitive

statement of the environmental information to be included. At the end of each appendix information is given about possible further sources of information. Again, these references can only be selective. However, it is expected that specialists will be aware of the most up-to-date guidance and publications in their field.

7. Collecting the information to be contained in an ES will frequently require specialist scientific and technical expertise. The responsibility for producing the ES is, of course, a matter for the developer, but it is strongly recommended that they involve or engage people with the necessary professional expertise to assist in its preparation.

8. The term 'environmental assessment' is generally taken to mean the whole process by which information about the environmental effects of a project is collected both by the developer and from other sources, including members of the public, and taken into account by the relevant authority in forming its judgement on whether the development should go ahead. **However, in this Guide,** EA is limited to that part of the process whereby the developer collects information about the environmental effects of a proposed development for assembly in an ES to be submitted with the application for planning permission.

9. Finally, this guide is not a guide to the law. Specific legal requirements relating to environmental assessment for projects requiring planning permission are set out in the EA Planning Regulations. A summary of the statutory framework is set out in **Table 1.** A detailed list of the Regulations applying to EA across all development consent procedures is to be found in Annex 1.

TABLE 1: The Statutory Framework for Environmental Assessment of Planning Projects

The principle EA Regulations relating to projects requiring planning permission are:

- for England & Wales:

  The Town & Country Planning (Assessment of Environmental Effects) Regulations 1988 (S.I. 1988/1199). These Regulations were amended by S.I. 1990/367, S.I. 1992/1494 and S.I. 1994/677.

- for Scotland:

  The Environmental Assessment (Scotland) Regulations 1988 (S.I. 1988/1221) These Regulations were amended by S.I. 1994/2012

Both sets of Regulations contain the following Schedules:

- **Schedule 1** lists categories of development for which EA is mandatory.
- **Schedule 2** lists a larger number of categories of development for which EA is required if the particular project would be likely to have significant effects on the environment.
- **Schedule 3** describes an environmental statement for the purpose of the Regulations. It sets out the **'specified information'** which must be provided as part of the ES, and also lists other information which may be included by way of explanation or amplification.

Formal guidance on these procedures, directed primarily at planning authorities, has been issued in:

- DOE Circular 15/88 (Welsh Office Circular 23/88) and SDD Circular 13/88 and SOEND Circular No. 26/1994

The Regulations set out the law, while the Circulars give guidance about EA and the preparation of ESs for planning projects.

PART

1

UNDERTAKING AN ENVIRONMENTAL ASSESSMENT

Chapter 1 PLANNING AN ENVIRONMENTAL ASSESSMENT

A systematic approach - defining the brief - determining the content - establishing a programme and timetable - assembling the project team - establishing environmental trends - considering existing plans and policies

EA: A SYSTEMATIC APPROACH

1.1 Planning authorities should always obtain the information they consider necessary to determine a planning application, including information about environmental effects. What is different about EA is the emphasis on the systematic analysis and presentation of information about environmental effects. The analysis should use the best practicable techniques and available sources of information. The presentation should be in a form which provides a focus for scrutiny of the project by those with specialist knowledge as well as non-expert decision makers and interested members of the public. It should also allow the importance of the predicted effects, and the scope for modifying or mitigating them, to be properly evaluated by the planning authority before a decision is taken.

1.2 To be systematic, the analysis should -

- through baseline studies examine the environmental character of the area likely to be affected by the development;
- identify relevant natural and manmade processes which may already be changing the character of the site;
- consider the possible interactions between the proposed development and both existing and future site conditions;
- predict the possible effects, both beneficial and adverse, of the development on the environment; and
- introduce design and operational modifications or other measures to avoid, minimise or mitigate adverse effects and enhance positive effects.

1.3 The analysis may indicate ways in which the project can be modified to anticipate likely adverse effects, (for example, through the identification of a better practicable environmental option)[1], or by considering alternative processes. If this is done, the formal planning approval stages are likely to be more straightforward. The

[1] The concept of Best Practicable Environmental Option (BPEO) is incorporated into Integrated Pollution Control (IPC) under the Environmental Protection Act 1990. For developments subject to IPC, applicants for IPC authorisation must demonstrate that the BPEO has been determined.

most effective environmental policy consists in preventing the creation of pollution or nuisances at source rather than subsequently trying to counteract their effects.

1.4 In practice, the level of attention given to individual environmental topics in an EA should reflect the significance of potential impacts and their importance to the decision making process. This, in turn, will determine the amount of background work which needs to be undertaken, the timescale for the studies, and the content, structure, and length of the ES, which are dealt with in Part II of this Guide.

DEFINING THE BRIEF

1.5 In planning an EA, the developer will need to balance a wide range of competing demands on resources of time and money. The requirements will include:

- determining the content of the EA;
- establishing a programme and timetable; and
- assembling the project team.

Determining the Content of the EA

1.6 The scope and content of the EA will be determined by the nature of the development proposal, the alternatives under consideration, and the range and complexity of the issues to be investigated. It is desirable to prepare a brief for an initial site appraisal and review of potential environmental concerns, leading to the production of a 'scoping' report. This document will describe the key environmental issues to be addressed in the EA and define the extent of "baseline" surveys required to establish existing environmental conditions on and surrounding the development site against which predictions about future change both with and without the project can be made.

1.7 Detailed technical studies covering aspects of the project's engineering feasibility and economic viability may have to run in parallel with the environmental baseline surveys. At critical stages in the EA, findings from these different studies can be drawn together to review options and to eliminate or refine alternatives. This leads ultimately to the selection of a preferred development option. The process of progressively refining the project design can be assisted in some cases by preparing a preliminary ES which is circulated within the project team and more widely, as appropriate.

Establishing a Programme and Timetable

1.8 A view should be taken at the outset of the length of time required to complete the different phases of work. This will be dictated in part by the stage at which the EA is initiated, the complexity of the proposals, commercial and financial constraints, and the need for original survey work. This may in turn be constrained by the weather or season of the year.

1.9 There is of course no absolute timetable for completing an environmental assessment. For a major EA it may run for 12-18 months from the decision to initiate the EA to production of the final ES. This reflects a situation where background information on, for example, flora and fauna, climatic conditions and noise and dust, may need to be collected over a full year in order to identify seasonal variations. For some schemes, for example, where river quality or air pollution may be involved, time will be required to reflect changes in weather and other conditions. Such requirements underline the benefits of initiating the EA early in the design of the project.

1.10 In other cases, particularly for smaller projects, the timescale for completing the EA may be shortened significantly where background information has already been collected in earlier studies, or where the number of environmental issues which are considered to be of direct relevance to the decision is small.

1.11 Figure 1 shows a typical timetable for an EA spread over a 12 month period. What appears as a simple linear progression of activities is, in practice, an iterative process of review, and evaluation as the planning and design of the project is progressively refined and improved.

FIGURE 1: Typical Timetable for EA

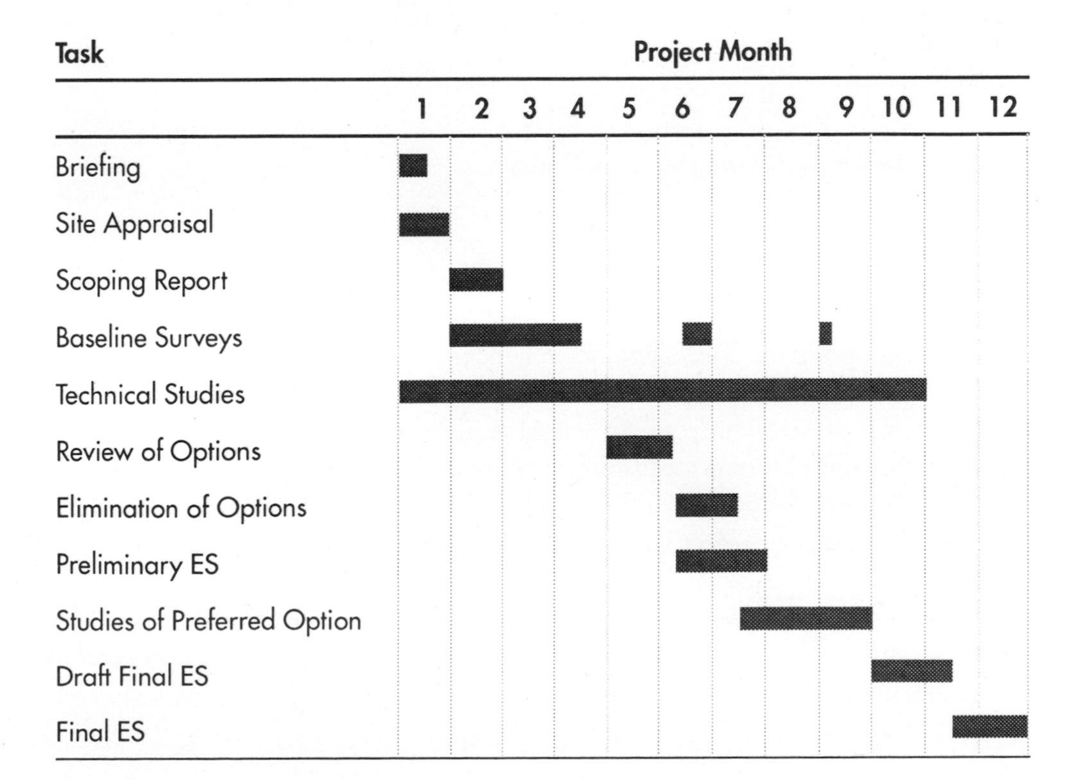

Assembling the Project Team

1.12 The developer will need to consider whether the necessary in-house resources and professional expertise are available to handle all stages of the work. Where this is not the case, or there is seen to be merit in having an external assessment, part or all of the work may be contracted out.

1.13 Where feasibility studies are led by individuals who are not trained in environmental planning, it may be appropriate to consider employing an environmental specialist within the design team who should be able to comment on the environmental implications of alternatives and design options, and to advise on the appropriate stage at which to launch a full EA.

1.14 Organisations drawing on 'in-house' project management and specialist environmental skills, should consider how to give those responsible for conducting the EA an identity which minimises any perceived risk of bias and lack of objectivity. A similar approach may also be appropriate for local authority staff involved in proposals where the authority is both the developer and the planning authority responsible for taking the decision on whether or not the project should proceed.

1.15 For those EAs involving large or complex proposals, it may be appropriate to appoint a project manager to oversee the conduct and production of the EA. The most important skills of the project manager are likely to be; experience of the full process of EA, an adequate training in methods and techniques, and previous experience in contributing to ESs. Typically, the role of the project manager would be to:

- co-ordinate the efforts of team members (who may be unrelated specialists based in different organisations);
- liaise with the developer, the design team, the local planning authority and other consultees and local community groups;
- integrate the specialist assessments within the ES;
- make critical judgements regarding the interactions between effects identified for the different topic areas; and,
- deliver the project within time and to cost.

1.16 The principal aim of the project manager will be to ensure that the work proceeds along the lines established during the scoping process and ensure that the conclusions of the EA are in a form that will be useful for the decision-making process.

ESTABLISHING ENVIRONMENTAL TRENDS

1.17 The environmental conditions on the site at the time of the baseline study will be examined in detail. But the processes of change that are occurring independently of the development are equally important. These processes will affect the environmental conditions and it is possible to forecast what conditions will prevail without the development. These future conditions are often called the "do-nothing" option and represent a useful baseline comparison.

1.18 Those undertaking the EA should establish what changes have occurred in the past and make a forecast of future trends over the lifetime of a project. Examples of such processes can include siltation in rivers, lakes and estuaries resulting from alterations in land use practices; changes in the composition of grasslands as a result of changes in farming regimes; and increases in traffic on local road networks. Forecasting the nature and rate of future change is not an exact science. It is important therefore that the assumptions and basis for any predictions are clearly defined and a realistic range of projections employed.

CONSIDERING EXISTING PLANS AND POLICIES

1.19 The plans and policies of local authorities and other bodies with major influence over land use and environmental quality standards (including the development plan for the area) should be carefully examined as part of the review of environmental trends. They should also serve as a basis for establishing what environmental conditions are likely to exist during the construction and operating stages of the project. There may, for example, be plans for new housing in the vicinity of the development site which would affect noise and other environmental health standards. The study of plans and policies provides the opportunity to identify those elements of a development proposal which conflict with, or support, established strategies. It may then be possible to introduce design modifications to minimise adverse effects, or to ameliorate or mitigate their consequences.

Chapter 2 PRELIMINARY PROCEDURES

Defining the scope of the EA - preliminary consultations - significant environmental issues - standard checklists and matrices - baseline studies - alternatives, need and demand - public consultation - project specification - defining requirements for baseline surveys

2.1 In order to carry out the process of analysis, appraisal and evaluation which lies at the heart of EA, a methodical approach, which would normally include the following stages, should be adopted.

DEFINING THE SCOPE OF THE EA

2.2 Defining its scope is one of the most critical parts of an EA in that it sets the context for what follows. If the scope is defined too narrowly, some critical area of uncertainty or adverse impact may emerge late in the day. Decisions on the shape of the project may then be too far advanced to allow for any real change. On the other hand, if the scope of the work is too loosely defined, then much time, effort and cost may be spent on pursuing unnecessary detail.

2.3 Effectively, scoping is the key to a good quality Environmental Statement. **Table 2** (summarised from a fuller list at **Appendix** 4 to **Environmental Assessment: A Guide to the Procedures**) offers an outline checklist of matters to be considered when defining the scope of the EA.

2.4 It is also important to be aware of other relevant procedures targeted at specific environmental issues. In particular, the integrated pollution control and local authority air pollution control systems established under Part I of the Environmental Protection Act 1990 both require an assessment of environmental consequences to accompany applications for authorisation. In order to minimise the costs and burdens imposed on business and any delays associated with negotiating separate applications consecutively, developers may avoid undesirable duplication by preparing them in parallel. Much of the information required for these two applications will be comparable.

2.5 A summary of the main pollution control systems is included in Planning Policy Guidance Note 23 - 'Planning and Pollution Control'.

2.6 In the case of developments which are likely to have a significant impact on the environment only in a clearly defined and limited field, the scoping exercise will permit subsequent work to be concentrated on one or two environmental topics.

TABLE 2 : Checklist of matters to be considered for inclusion when scoping an EA

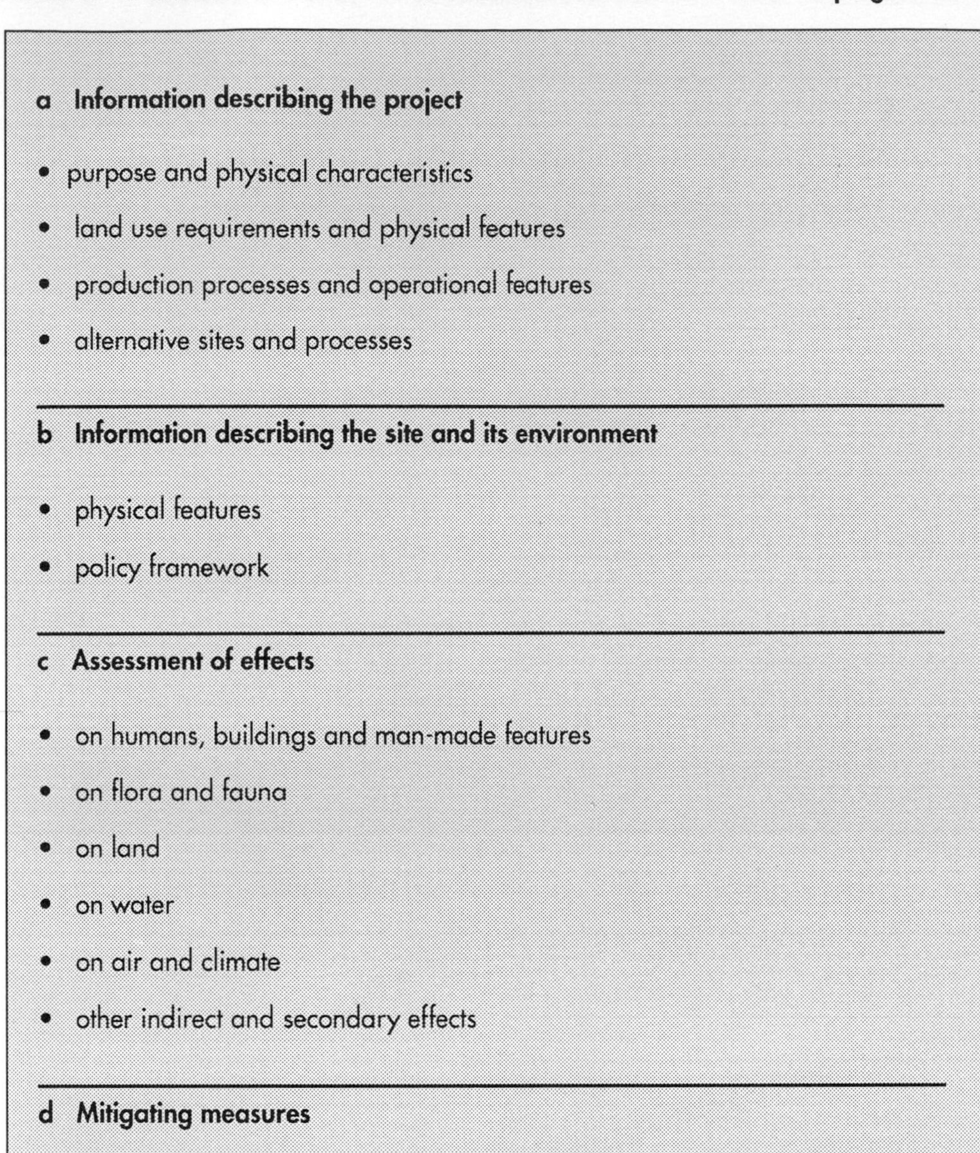

a Information describing the project

- purpose and physical characteristics
- land use requirements and physical features
- production processes and operational features
- alternative sites and processes

b Information describing the site and its environment

- physical features
- policy framework

c Assessment of effects

- on humans, buildings and man-made features
- on flora and fauna
- on land
- on water
- on air and climate
- other indirect and secondary effects

d Mitigating measures

e Risks of accidents and hazardous development

2.7 The main function of the scoping exercise will be to confirm the nature of the development, the breadth of the EA, the range of key issues and the extent to which each environmental topic area needs to be investigated. It will also start to define the areas of physical survey required, although this can only be confirmed once the baseline studies have been initiated.

Preliminary Consultations

2.8 The Circulars and Guide to Procedures recommend that developers proposing projects should have full and early consultation with both the planning authority and other bodies which have an interest in the likely environmental effects. The planning authority and statutory consultees[1] should be invited to participate in defining the terms of reference of the EA. They may have specific knowledge or information about the site and may be able to offer the benefits of their experience and expertise. If the nature of the proposals and timing of the EA pose problems of commercial confidentiality, preliminary consultations may be done through informal and confidential discussion.

Significant Environmental Issues

2.9 The range of environmental issues or topics which are relevant in any particular circumstance will reflect the nature of the proposals, their scale and their location. For example, activities like mineral extraction, waste disposal through landfill, and road construction often have the potential to affect the water environment; whereas power generation and incineration raise important questions about air and climate. As a general rule, the larger the site area affected by a development the more likely it is that significant environmental effects will result; but the nature and location of the development are more important considerations. Proposed developments located within, or adjacent to, areas designated for their nature conservation, landscape, geological, or archaeological importance, (such as National Parks, National Scenic Areas, conservation areas, etc) require careful scrutiny.

2.10 The identification of key environmental issues may be based upon:

- Use of standard checklists and matrices;
- Use of independent advisers; or,
- Preliminary consultation with statutory bodics.

Use of Standard Checklists and Matrices

2.11 A range of methods exist to assist the developer or the assessment team define the scope of an EA. These include the use of checklists and matrices such as that at Figure 2, in chapter 7.

2.12 Where checklists and matrices are used, it is desirable that individual members of the assessment team should fill in their perceptions of the critical areas of potential impact, based on past knowledge and experience. It may also be helpful to ask the planning authority to comment on the checklist or matrix independently. Any difference in emphasis can then be identified and areas of disagreement resolved through discussion.

[1] For England and Wales, a list of statutory consultees is given in Article 10 of the Town and Country Planning (General Development Procedure) Order 1995, and the EA Regulations. For Scotland, see Schedule 4 to the Environmental Assessment (Scotland)Regulations 1988.

The Content of Baseline Studies

2.13 A comparison of the details of the development proposal with what is known about the environmental conditions of the site and its surroundings should identify the nature of baseline studies required. It will then be necessary to decide what level of detail is needed on individual topics such as water, air, ecology and landscape. This raises the question of significance since the EA Planning Regulations (Schedule 3, paragraph 2) require that the ES should contain:

- the data necessary to identify and assess the **main effects** which the development is likely to have on the environment;
- a description of the likely **significant effects**, direct and indirect, on the environment of the development; and
- where **significant adverse effects** are identified, a description of the measures envisaged in order to avoid, reduce or remedy those effects. (**see Table** 7)

2.14 Paragraph 3(e) of Schedule 3 to the EA Planning Regulations provides that the description of likely significant direct and indirect effects may include secondary, cumulative, short, medium and long-term, permanent, temporary, positive and negative effects. The inclusion of positive or beneficial effects, as well as negative or adverse ones, is important since a balanced EA should give due weight to both types of impact.

Consideration of Alternatives, Need and Demand

2.15 Another issue which should be addressed in the scoping exercise is how to handle alternatives, need and demand. It is generally the case that the main opportunities for considering alternative courses of action, and even different development sites and processes, arise in the early stages of a new project. Very often, decisions on the range of alternatives to be considered will need to be taken with only a basic amount of detailed information at the feasibility study stage. Environmental issues will be one of the factors influencing the choice, and they will need to be balanced against technical feasibility and cost.

2.16 In the EA Planning Regulations, the consideration of alternatives is not included within the 'specified information' which must be contained in an ES. However, it is included in paragraph 3(d) of Schedule 3, as part of the further information which may be included by way of explanation or amplification of the specified information (**see Table** 7) and it is generally helpful to show what alternatives, if any, have been considered.

2.17 The Guide to Procedures highlights the benefits of starting the EA at the stage of site selection and, where relevant, process selection. This allows for the practical consideration of alternatives and helps to avoid delay if important issues emerge later.

2.18 There are certain types of project for which the issue of alternatives is more restricted, such as the extraction of a mineral ore which can only be mined in situ. However, even in this case there may be opportunities for varying the location of processing plant, access routes or power transmission lines serving the site. In other examples, like the planning of a new reservoir, there may be a number of potential options. If the environmental principles contributing to the elimination of variants are carefully recorded at the time of the decision, this will greatly improve the credibility and overall objectivity of the eventual ES.

2.19 There is no requirement in the EA Regulations that a developer should demonstrate a proven need or demand for the project when producing an ES. In many cases, the question of need or demand will be dealt with under other licensing or authorisation procedures. In others, the issue will be irrelevant to the basic question of the extent to which the project may or may not have significant effects on the environment. However, demand for energy and natural resources, and the effects of their consumption on the overall state of the environment, are recognised as increasingly important. Where need and demand are shown to have direct links to environmental quality, these may be material considerations in the context of the planning decision.

Deciding on the Role of Public Consultation

2.20 While developers are under no obligation to publicise their proposals before submitting a planning application, consultation with local amenity groups and with the general public can be useful in identifying key environmental issues. Such consultation may put the developer in a better position to modify the project in ways which would mitigate adverse effects and recognise local environmental concerns. It will also give the developer an early indication of the issues which are likely to be important at the formal application stage if, for instance, the proposal goes to public inquiry.

2.21 It is at the scoping stage that the developer should consider the most appropriate point at which to involve members of the public. Developers may be reluctant to make a public announcement about their proposals at an early stage, perhaps because of commercial concerns relating to land purchase negotiations or perceived challenges from rival companies. There may also be occasions when public disclosure of development proposals in advance of a formal planning application may cause unnecessary blight. However, early announcement of plans for prospecting and site or route selection, and the provision of opportunities for environmental/amenity groups and local people to comment on environmental issues, may channel legitimate concerns into constructive criticism.

PREPARING A PROJECT SPECIFICATION

2.22 Promoters of a project will wish to ensure that those concerned with its design and those concerned with the EA work closely together. It is at this stage in the project's evolution that the greatest opportunity exists for minimising adverse effects and maximising environmental benefits.

2.23 One way to encourage this is to prepare a project specification which:

- describes what is known about the requirements of the project;
- identifies the range of uncertainty applying to specific aspects of the design; and,
- starts to spell out potential environmental impacts.

2.24 For example, the project specification might contain an estimate of the volume of material to be transported and the number of vehicle movements likely to be generated in an average week. Such information will provide the EA team with the basis for examining potential disturbance to local communities from traffic movement and noise, and for making recommendations on ways of minimising nuisance and inconvenience. Project specifications should be updated at regular intervals as the design of the project is modified and redefined.

DEFINING REQUIREMENTS FOR ENVIRONMENTAL BASELINE SURVEYS

2.25 As a result of the scoping exercise, a picture should emerge of the environmental issues to be investigated in baseline surveys. These are likely to include the site of the development, its access and any other areas likely to be disturbed during construction and operation.

2.26 However, the boundaries of study areas may need to extend over much wider areas to encompass the full range of direct and indirect environmental impacts which could follow from development. For example, landscape surveys will usually include the zone of visual influence - generally all land which is visually linked with the development site. Hydrological and ecological surveys may need to follow streams or river courses for considerable distances downstream (and possibly upstream) depending upon judgements about the concentrations and likely dispersal patterns of effluent to be discharged from the new facility. Thus, the definition of baseline survey areas is an extension of the scoping process and may need to be refined progressively as information comes to light.

Chapter 3 PREDICTING IMPACTS AND FORMULATING MITIGATING MEASURES

Identifying potential impacts - describing resources and receptors - cause and effect - predicting the nature and extent of impacts and magnitude of effects - selecting methods of prediction - uncertainty - fact, judgement and opinion - mitigating adverse effects - evaluating impacts - hazard and risk assessment

3.1 Impact prediction involves the analysis of potential causes of change to the existing environment and determination of likely effects. The magnitude or physical extent of predicted impacts should be presented in quantifiable terms wherever possible.

3.2 The basic stages of impact prediction are:

- identifying the activities in the development process likely to generate impacts, both positive and negative;
- identify resources and receptors likely to be affected by those impacts;
- establish the chain of events or pathways linking cause with effect;
- predict the likely nature, extent and magnitude of any anticipated changes or effects;
- evaluate the consequences of any impacts identified; and,
- establish which potential impacts (positive or negative) should be regarded as significant.

Identifying Potential Impacts

3.3 The scoping stage of the EA should have identified the key topic areas in which the development has the potential to cause either adverse or beneficial effects on the environment. Each of these elements should be reviewed in terms of its capacity to affect the environmental baseline conditions (including environmental trends and anticipated changes). Manuals and guidelines produced for specific types of development may be useful here.

3.4 There is extensive literature in the technical press on methods which may be used to examine potential impacts, including networks, matrices and systems analysis. Illustrative guidance relating to individual environmental topics is set out in the Appendices to this Guide.

Describing Resources and Receptors

3.5 Development projects may affect only a few discrete areas of the environment, or they may affect a complete ecosystem or geographical region. While it is important that the environment should be considered as a single entity, it is usually convenient to subdivide potential and predicted impacts by topic. These may be physical resources like water or soil, or individual species of plants or animals which become the receptors of specific impacts.

3.6 The EA Planning Regulations require the ES to include environmental topics covering human beings, flora, fauna, soil, water, air, climate and landscape. They also require it to include the interaction between these factors and to examine the effects on material assets and the cultural heritage.

3.7 'Material assets' is not defined in the EA Planning Regulations (nor in the EIA Directive). The term is generally taken to include buildings and other man-made artefacts (although that is not an exhaustive definition). Thus, although 'material assets' and the 'cultural heritage' appear as separate topics in Schedule 3 to the EA Planning Regulations, they are treated in this Guide as a single topic area. The term may be further clarified as a result of amendments to the EIA Directive currently under discussion.

3.8 Within this framework, it often helps to consider each topic under a number of different sub-headings (see **Table 3** and Note).

3.9 In assessing potential impacts, it is desirable to note the distinction between **processes** which give rise to impacts and the **effects** which such impacts have on the basic resource or receptor. For example, it is now possible to use sophisticated equipment to predict increases in sound from mechanical plant and the scope for reducing or attenuating the resulting noise levels. But what matters in the final analysis is how these changes in noise level will affect human beings and/or fauna. The answer will depend upon many varied factors. Since it is usually impracticable to assess the effects of noise on every individual, 'target' groups are selected such as people working in immediate contact with the source, or living within a specified distance, or engaging in a particular recreational activity.

3.10 Another example of the use of 'target' groups is the identification of 'indicator species' in studies of flora and fauna. Salmonoid fish, for example, are particularly sensitive to oxygen levels and heavy metals in water. If these fish are present in a watercourse where effluent discharges from the development will not give rise to concentrations of pollutants which would harm these species, it may be assumed that more tolerant species will also be unaffected.

TABLE 3: Example List of Environmental Topics

EA Planning Regulations Environmental Topics	Example Sub-headings *
Human Beings	population housing noise and vibration air/water and land pollution infrastructure/services land use - agriculture - recreation - forestry - mineral resources - waste disposal
Flora and Fauna	habitats plant and animal communities individual species
Soil	geology geomorphology agricultural land quality
Water	hydrological cycle surface water ground water coastal/estuarine
Air and Climate	heat, chemical, odorous and gaseous emissions particulate matter
Landscape	landform/topography land use land cover landscape character landscape quality
Cultural Heritage and Material Assets	architectural interest archaeological interest historic interest ancient monuments

* Note: This list is not intended to be exhaustive; nor will all the sub-headings be relevant in every case.

Examining Pathways Linking Cause with Effect

3.11 The links between sources of pollution (or the initial cause of an impact) and the receptor may be direct or indirect. Substances dispersed in flue gases from a chimney can, for example, have a direct effect on vegetation or they may be dissolved in water before affecting their ultimate receptor. Pollutants generally become more dilute as they are dispersed from source but there are circumstances where they can become re-concentrated in living tissues as they pass along the food chain. Linkages between pathways must also be considered since changes in one medium can affect another. Changes in water temperature, for example, can influence rates of chemical diffusion and absorption.

3.12 Analysis of pathways may lead to the identification of successive changes which may be described as first, second and third order impacts. For example, an increase in suspended solids in water can reduce light penetration, slowing down the rate of photosynthesis in algae and providing less food for fish. This results in fewer and smaller specimens and might lead ultimately to the decline of a commercial fishery. In this case, water, fauna and human beings are **all** affected either directly or indirectly by the changes.

Predicting the Nature and Extent of Impacts and the Magnitude of their Effects

3.13 Each of the impacts identified in the course of the EA needs to be considered in terms of its basic nature, the physical extent of its influence, and the magnitude of its effects. In considering the nature of impacts it will be necessary to assess whether the effects will be:

- direct or indirect
- short, medium or long-term
- reversible or irreversible
- beneficial or adverse
- cumulative.

These criteria are also relevant when evaluating the significance of an impact, discussed in paragraphs 3.24-3.28.

3.14 For example, the **nature of the impact** arising from discharging heated water from a power station will be an increase in the average temperature of the receiving watercourse. This will have direct long-term impacts with both adverse and beneficial effects. The **physical extent** of the impact will be dependent on the relative volumes of water involved and the degree of mixing which occurs. In a large estuary the effects may be dissipated rapidly over a very wide area, leading to only a slight increase in temperature. In a river or lake, the effects may be more confined leading to appreciable rises in temperature. The **magnitude** of the effects in both cases will depend upon the baseline ecological conditions of the receiving water, and any critical thresholds in the tolerance of plants and organisms to increases in temperature. If there is more than one power station on a river, their individual impacts on water temperature may be slight but the cumulative effects could be significant.

Selecting Methods of Prediction

3.15 Methods of prediction will differ according to the environmental topic under investigation. They will often include a combination of qualitative and quantitative techniques, as in the assessment of noise pollution illustrated in **Table 4.**

3.16 **Qualitative** techniques rely heavily on previous experience and knowledge of the consequences of certain types of action. **Quantitative** techniques usually seek to model the natural environment. Examples of modelling include the analysis of the time and concentration of storm run-off from an urban catchment; the dispersal patterns and dilution of flue gases from chimney stacks; and the distribution of noise contours around an airport. With such models it is possible to derive confidence limits relating to the accuracy of the predictions. Other effects are more difficult to quantify since they may result from poorly understood pathways and/or inadequate data. The extent and limitations of current knowledge should be clearly stated in any predictions.

TABLE 4: Example of Assessment of Noise Pollution

A Typical Assessment of Noise Pollution will involve
establishing the ambient noise levels by day and night around the site through baseline surveys;
obtaining (from manufacturer's specifications, or existing developments) a full spectral analysis of noise outputs for the types of equipment and plant proposed on the site;
calculating the increased (or decreased) noise levels which will rise at point (or linear) sources within the site;
calculating the degree of noise attenuation afforded by distance, screening or other mitigating measures between the point of origin and the receiver;
predicting the increase in resultant noise levels;
relating the findings to established standards for noise control in industrial or residential areas or to other yardsticks where standards are not available (eg noise in the countryside);
estimating the number of people and types and locations of fauna directly or indirectly affected by increases in noise of varying intensity.

Dealing with Uncertainty

3.17 Uncertainty may arise in the course of an EA in trying to predict:

- the probability of an event occurring;
- the severity of the event, when it occurs;
- the consequences stemming from an event; and,
- interactions between two or more events.

The reliability of the methods used to carry out the above assessments may also be uncertain.

For most studies it will be sufficient to note the degree of uncertainty attached to different predictions. But where health and safety is a major issue, full hazard and risk assessment may be required as part of a separate study. (See 3.29-3.31)

Fact, Judgement, and Opinions

3.18 The analysis of environmental impacts usually involves a progression from matters of fact, which can be stated with certainty, through a process of scientific appraisal or professional judgement, to the expression of opinions on the relative significance of the findings. A clear distinction should be drawn between matters of fact, judgements and opinions, and all sources identified.

3.19 One of the merits of an ES in which these elements are clearly presented is that agreement can usually be reached between the developer, planning authority and interested parties on the substantive facts, leaving any debate to the interpretations to be placed on those facts. If there is confusion, the scope for argument and potential delay is much greater.

REFINING THE PROPOSALS TO MITIGATE ADVERSE EFFECTS

3.20 A fundamental aim of using EA procedures as an integral part of the design process is to ensure that potentially damaging effects are avoided or minimised and the beneficial aspects are enhanced. This process will usually take place in a continuous cycle as the proposals for the development are refined. Consultation with pollution control authorities will be an important aspect of identifying suitable mitigation measures, particularly since authorisation conditions for pollution control will fall primarily to HMIP[1] (HMIPI[1] in Scotland) to determine

[1] As from 1st April 1996, in England and Wales the Environment Agency will take over the functions of Her Majesty's Inspectorate of Pollution and in Scotland the Scottish Environment Protection Agency will take over the functions of Her Majesty's Industrial Pollution Inspectorate

(in the case of IPC processes). Three types of mitigation may be considered:

- avoidance;
- reduction;
- remedy.

3.21 The most satisfactory form of mitigation is to **avoid** environmental damage at source through re-design. **Reduction** involves lessening the severity of an impact which cannot be avoided entirely. **Remedy** (which may include **enhancement** or **compensation**) acknowledges that some adverse consequences will stem from the development, but provides means by which the conditions can be improved or compensated for.

3.22 **Table 5** provides some examples of what these might mean in practice.

TABLE 5: Examples of Mitigating Measures

	Avoidance	Reduction	Remedy
Noise	Use an inherently quieter machine	Fit sound insulation around the machine	Provide or pay for double glazing on nearby houses
Effluent	Change process to eliminate effluent	Either change to a process with a lower toxicity of effluent or apply onsite treatment	Discharge effluent through a long outfall where it will have less effect
Woodland	Redesign site layout to prevent adverse effects	Modify proposals to minimise tree felling	Plant new woodland

3.23 An ES should make clear which elements of the development have been introduced to mitigate potential adverse effects.

EVALUATING IMPACTS AND THEIR EFFECTS

3.24 One of the most important parts of the EA process is to attach some measure of significance to impact predictions. Environmental quality standards may provide a framework for evaluation where these lay down acceptable and unacceptable limits of polluting substances in air or water. If, for example, it can be shown that emissions to air will not lead to increases in gases in excess of the natural variation in the range of concentrations, then the effects might be described as **insignificant.** If, on the other hand, gaseous emissions are predicted to result in detectable increases in concentrations, although still falling below permissible legal limits, the results might be described as **minor** or of **some significance.** Emissions which are likely to result in a breach of a legally defined value would clearly be of **major significance**.

3.25 There are also accepted methods for measuring the impacts of noise and traffic, and for relating these to thresholds of tolerance, or carrying capacities. It is more difficult to produce evaluation frameworks for intangible assets like the public perception of landscape value. However, it is possible to reach a consensus through 'panel' interviews and other sampling techniques.

3.26 The evaluation process will usually involve considering the significance of an impact under a number of criteria:

- extent and magnitude;
- short-term and long-term;
- reversibility and irreversibility;
- performance against environmental quality standards;
- sensitivity of the receptor;
- compatibility with environmental policies.

3.27 It may sometimes be helpful to attach scores to criteria to indicate levels of significance. Scaling and weighting can be useful in distinguishing between the relative impacts of alternatives. For example, in assessing the effect which three different pipeline routes would have on the ecology of a particular area, one set of values might relate to the length of pipeline crossing heathland, which once disturbed takes a long time to restore; another might relate to designations such as SSSI or AONB; a third could involve lengths of pipeline crossing high quality agricultural land. By altering the relative weight attached to each of these (and other) criteria, the relative sensitivity of the routes can be assessed. This method of analysis can be open to criticism that the scales and weights are subjective. Sensitivity tests should therefore be carried out on the scales and weights attached to the different criteria.

3.28 When setting up the framework for evaluating impacts, care should be taken to identify the practical limitations of the methods proposed. Quantitative methods which seek to establish a single index of environmental values are unlikely to assist the decision-maker who needs to make the ultimate choice between social, economic and environmental consequences of a new development proposal. On the other hand, some individual elements of an assessment can benefit from the application of quantitative techniques, especially in the fields of air and water pollution, and ecology. Although there is renewed interest in seeking to attach monetary values to environmental impacts methods of economic evaluation are still in the early stages of development. Some of these are reviewed in '**Policy Appraisal and the Environment**' published by HMSO for the Department of the Environment.

Hazard and Risk Assessment

3.29 In addition to the tasks listed above, it may be appropriate to consider hazard and risk assessment.

3.30 Identification of **hazards** calls for the systematic examination of all elements of the project's design and their interactions with the environment to determine how harm might arise. Examples include:

- natural hazards such as land instability and flooding;
- failure of engineered structures under stress such as dams;
- malfunctioning of plant and equipment, causing accidental release of toxic, inflammable or explosive chemicals.

As there is a chance these circumstances will actually occur, **risk assessment** may be needed.

3.31 These processes requires specialist knowledge and skills for their execution. Guidance on them is available in the publications "A Guide to Risk Assessment and Risk Management for Environmental Protection", published in June 1995 and "Policy Appraisal and the Environment" first published in 1991. Both publications are available through HMSO.

PART

2

PREPARING AN ENVIRONMENTAL STATEMENT

Chapter 4 ASSEMBLING THE ENVIRONMENTAL STATEMENT

Alternative approaches - structure and content - method statement - length - scoping study - non-technical summary

4.1 The Environmental Statement (ES) is the most visible part of the EA process. It draws together the findings of the developer's technical studies prior to the submission of a planning application. It is the developer's responsibility to prepare the ES and present the information in a comprehensive, clear and objective manner for review by the planning authority and statutory consultees. It **must** include a non-technical summary to assist in the process of public consultation.

4.2 By the time the task of assembling the ES is begun work should have been completed on:

- defining the scope of the EA;
- undertaking baseline studies;
- assessing trends; and
- considering policy and plan implications.

Preliminary findings should also have emerged from:

- analysis of potential impacts;
- predicting and evaluating the magnitude and significance of impacts; and
- proposing mitigating measures.

However, the full effects of a project will often only emerge as the inter-relationships between environmental topic areas become clear, following completion of the specialist studies. It may therefore be useful to prepare a 'draft' statement for internal consideration as part of the overall study programme.

ALTERNATIVE APPROACHES TOWARDS PREPARING AN ES

4.3. The approach chosen will depend upon the particular circumstances relating to the project, its environmental setting and the organisation of the EA team.

4.4 One way is for the contributions on particular topic areas to be written by individual specialists. They subsequently remain responsible for the precise wording of the text even though an editor will be responsible for the assembly of the document. If this method is used it is important that the linkages between subject areas are properly explored and covered. This can be done either in supplementary sections or in a single chapter written by the editor. These are both effective ways to draw together the different specialist inputs. Without this editorial input the end product may appear as a loose collection of unrelated and sometimes contradictory statements and it may fail to meet the requirement to describe the interaction between the main effects.

4.5 Another approach to writing an ES involves using just one author, preferably with experience in EA. He or she is responsible for reviewing the findings of the individual specialists and then writing the entire document, drawing on the working papers. This has the advantage that the author can cross-check and cross-reference all the material, highlight key issues, eliminate irrelevant detail and give the report a consistent style. On the other hand, there is a risk that some issues may be over-simplified in the process. If this approach is adopted it is important that the individual specialists should see and approve the text which is produced from their own work before publication.

4.6 A third approach, representing an intermediate position, involves the collation of individual specialist reports in a volume of appendices while the 'main report' is written by one author. This clarifies the individual responsibilities of the production team. But the editor should take care not to add unduly to the length of the document through duplication.

STRUCTURE AND CONTENT OF THE ES

4.7 There are no statutory requirements concerning the form of an ES but it must contain the information specified in paragraph 2 of Schedule 3 to the EA Planning Regulations. It may also include the further information set out in paragraph 3 of Schedule 3 by way of explanation or amplification. Schedule 3 is reproduced in Table 7. Although there is no prescribed format for an ES, the structure given as an example in Table 6 may help ensure all the relevant issues are covered.

4.8 If a planning authority consider an ES that has been submitted to be inadequate, they may write to the developer requiring further information concerning any matter mentioned in Schedule 3. That further information has to be reasonably required to enable the authority to give proper consideration to the likely environmental effects of the proposed development. The authority may also require a developer to produce evidence to verify information in the ES.

4.9 Where the ES comprises more than one document, the status of each and its relationship to the others should be clearly identified on the covers. The format and content of individual chapters in the ES will necessarily vary with different

TABLE 6: An Outline Structure for an Environmental Statement

1. A Non Technical Summary, which may also be available as a separate document
2. Method Statement
3. Statement of Key Issues
4. Description of the Project
5. Description of Environmental Conditions within and surrounding the site
6. Assessment of Environmental Effects by Topic Area, as set out in table 7 , 2c (Each chapter should identify baseline conditions, potential impacts, the scope for amelioration and/or mitigation of impacts, and provide a description of unavoidable impacts).
7. Appendices of technical data

types of project; the relative size and complexity of individual developments; and the nature of the significant effects. In practice the level of attention given to individual environmental topics in the ES should reflect the significance of the potential impacts and their importance to the decision-making process.

METHOD STATEMENT

4.10 The planning authority may look for information about who has written the ES, how it was prepared and what studies were undertaken to justify its conclusions. This information is not a formal requirement of the EA Planning Regulations but its inclusion in a **method statement** can save time by reducing the work of the planning authority and statutory consultees when they review the ES.

4.11 Ideally a method statement takes the reader through the background to the project. It describes, where applicable, the relationships between the promoter, the planning, engineering and design teams, and the company or individuals responsible for the ES. It also outlines the steps taken to determine the scope of the assessment and deals with the programme and timetable of the technical studies.

4.12 A method statement may also discuss the level of contact between those preparing the ES and statutory consultees. It may note any meetings, exhibitions or surveys involving the general public, and explain how issues like alternatives and objectivity have been dealt with. It discusses the approach taken towards determining the scale and significance of impacts, and the basis on which predictions have been made. Finally it should make clear what guidelines, methods or techniques have been used in the process.

TABLE 7 : Content of An Environmental Statement

The following are the statutory provisions with respect to the content of environmental statements, as set out in Schedule 3 to the Town and Country Planning (Assessment of Environmental Effects) Regulations 1988 and the Environmental Assessment (Scotland) Regulations 1988.

1. An environmental statement comprises a document or series of documents providing for the purpose of assessing the likely impact upon the environment of the development proposed to be carried out, the information specified in paragraph 2 (referred to in this Schedule as "the specified information").

---

2. The specified information is -
   a. a description of the development proposed, comprising information about the site and the design and size or scale of the development;
   b. the data necessary to identify and assess the main effects which the development is likely to have on the environment;
   c. a description of the likely significant effects, direct and indirect, on the environment of the development, explained by reference to its possible impact on:
      human beings;
      flora;
      fauna;
      soil;
      water;
      air;
      climate;
      the landscape;
      the inter-action between any of the foregoing;
      material assets;
      the cultural heritage;
   d. where significant adverse effects are identified with respect to any of the foregoing, a description of the measures envisaged in order to avoid, reduce or remedy those effects; and
   e. a summary in non-technical language of the information specified in sub-paragraphs (a) to (d).

---

3. An environmental statement may include, by way of explanation or amplification of the specified information, further information on any of the following matters -
   a. the physical characteristics of the proposed development, and the land-use requirements during the construction and operational phases;
   b. the main characteristics of the production processes proposed, including the nature and quality of the materials to be used;
   c. the estimated type and quantity of expected residues and emissions (including pollutants of water, air or soil, noise, vibration, light, heat and radiation) resulting from the proposed development when in operation;
   d. (in outline) the main alternatives (if any) studied by the applicant, appellant or authority and an indication of the main reasons for choosing the development proposed, taking into account environmental effects;
   e. the likely significant direct and indirect effects on the environment of the development proposed which may result from -
      i. the use of natural resources;
      ii. the emission of pollutants, the creation of nuisances, and the elimination of waste;
   f. the forecasting methods used to assess any effects on the environment about which information is given under sub-paragraph (e); and
   g. any difficulties, such as technical deficiencies or lack of know-how encountered in compiling any item of specified information.

   In paragraph (e), "effects" includes secondary, cumulative, short, medium and long term, permanent, temporary, positive and negative effects.

---

4. Where further information is included in an environmental statement pursuant to paragraph 3, a non-technical summary of that information shall also be provided.

LENGTH OF ENVIRONMENTAL STATEMENTS

4.13 For projects which involve a single site and relatively few areas of significant impact, it should be possible to produce a robust ES of around 50 pages. Where more complex issues arise, the main body of the statement may extend to 100 pages or so. If it exceeds 150 pages it is likely to become cumbersome and difficult to assimilate and this should generally be regarded as a maximum. Any additional information should be incorporated in appendices.

4.14 However, the quality of an ES will not be determined by its length. What is needed is a concise, objective analysis which deals with all the significant areas of impact and highlights the key issues relevant to the decision.

SCOPING STUDY

4.15 The findings of the scoping study should eventually be incorporated in the ES by indicating which topics were singled out for detailed investigation as 'key issues' (see the noise example at **Table** 4) and which topics were shown at an early stage to be of minor or no significance.

4.16 The reasons for conclusions on the level of significance included in the study should be spelled out clearly. This will allow the planning authority to verify them for itself and ensure that any discussion is focused on the key issues. (See 5.10)

NON-TECHNICAL SUMMARY

4.17 The EA Planning Regulations require a non-technical summary to be produced as part of the ES. Its purpose is to ensure that the findings of the studies undertaken can more readily be disseminated to the general public, and that the conclusions are easily understood by non-experts and decisions makers. It is therefore essential that the non-technical summary provides an accurate and balanced statement of key information contained in the ES.

4.18 It should describe all the conclusions of the ES, and the facts and judgements on which they are based. It is good practice to write short summaries and conclusions at the end of each section or chapter of the main statement which can then be carried forward and incorporated in the non-technical summary. This has the advantage that the same wording is used to define key issues and conclusions in both parts of the documents. It may also be helpful to present an overall summary table which records the relative weights attached to the significance of individual impacts; an example is given in **Figure 2** (see **Chapter** 7).

4.19 The non-technical summary is likely to have a higher public profile than the main report and may be printed in large numbers for public circulation. However, it should not be treated simply as a public relations document. Although the developer can take the opportunity to demonstrate an awareness of environmental issues, he or she should avoid the risk that bias may be introduced in an effort to highlight the proposal's most favourable features and play down adverse effects.

4.20 The non-technical summary may be bound into the main report or be produced as a separate document. There is no requirement for it to be available as a separate document, but to ensure adequate public consultation and a wider appreciation of the project and its environmental effects there may be clear benefits in doing so.

Chapter 5 THE PROJECT AND EXISTING ENVIRONMENTAL CONDITIONS

Describing the project - characteristics - phasing - alternatives - level of description - existing conditions - selection of material - environmental trends

THE PROJECT

5.1 A key element of an ES is the description of the proposed development. This should provide a comprehensive picture of the scheme, its purpose, location and scale. The project description should also describe the alternatives, if any, that have been considered. The function of the proposed development should be outlined and set in its economic and operational context. The account should be concise, with any necessary detail appearing later in the ES.

Characteristics

5.2 An introduction to the character of the site is needed to establish the context for the development. Further descriptions will usually be provided under chapters of the ES dealing with individual environmental topics.

5.3 The physical layout of the development including the siting and design of the buildings should be described. This should be done not only with written text but using maps, drawings, sketches, photomontage and computer simulations, where appropriate. This helps to present a clear visual impression of the development's appearance.

Phasing of the Development

5.4 The importance of describing the sequence of development is often overlooked but this is critical to the assessment of the project's potential effects during construction and operation, and in some cases during decommissioning. Where a significant time lapse is likely to occur between phases of the development, it may be useful to divide the ES into sections dealing with each phase in turn. The level of accuracy in predicting the effects of environmental change is likely to decline, the further into the future the works are planned.

Alternatives

5.5 Although discussion of alternatives is not required environmental information specified in Schedule 3 of the EA regulations (see table 7), it is generally helpful to say in the ES what alternatives, if any, have been considered. In the case of development proposals which have no alternative site, different options are likely to have been considered for features like earthworks, the siting and design of buildings, routing of roads, and cables and pipelines. In such cases the ES can help to reduce misinformed criticism of a project by spelling out the range of options considered and demonstrating how environmental factors have been taken into account in the design process.

LEVEL OF DESCRIPTION

5.6 Skill is needed in writing up the project in non-technical language for the benefit of the lay reader, while still providing sufficient detail to ensure that the processes and nature of the proposed plant and equipment can be fully understood. Technical summaries may need to be rewritten or expanded because features of the plant which are self-evident to the expert may mean little or nothing to others. This exercise of translating technical functions and operations into everyday language may highlight why a process, which the project designer may regard as routine, has the potential to cause significant environmental damage.

5.7 While every ES is likely to be based on a unique set of development characteristics, the list in **Table 8** provides an indication of some of the subjects which should be considered when drafting the Project Description.

EXISTING BASELINE ENVIRONMENTAL CONDITIONS

5.8 It is helpful to provide a general description of the environmental character of the development site and its surroundings at an early stage in the ES. This provides the context for the analysis which follows. More detailed observations on baseline conditions may be included or can follow in the introductions to chapters dealing with specific environmental topics.

5.9 The description of environmental conditions should refer to the scoping stage of the EA and the basis on which the alternative study areas were defined (see Chapter 3).

SELECTION OF MATERIAL

5.10 The EA Regulations provide that the environmental topics should include human beings, flora, fauna, soil, water, air, climate, landscape, material assets and the cultural heritage. The significance of the different environmental topics will vary according to the location and type of development under consideration (see **Appendices 1 - 10** for more detail). Information which does not relate directly to the areas of concern highlighted by the scoping process, and which does not indicate a further likely significant effects upon the environment, may obscure the conclusions of the analysis and need not be included. However, for completeness, and so that the local planning authority is aware that the likely environmental effects of the development on all of these topic areas have been considered, the ES should make it clear why they are not being discussed in detail.

5.11 Where the presentation of baseline environmental information necessitates the use of a considerable amount of data, it will often be appropriate to include the data in **appendices.** This limits the contents of the ES itself. Concentrating attention on those topic areas identified as being of relevance will help ensure that they are examined in sufficient detail. The aims will be to establish an objective picture of environmental conditions, and to describe the character, extent, importance and vulnerability of the various components of the environment.

5.12 The best available **sources** of data should be used. Where necessary, additional survey work should be described. Data sources should be clearly stated and methods of data collection described so that their validity can be established. Any limitations in the data or the use of information which cannot be verified should be clearly stated.

ENVIRONMENTAL TRENDS

5.13 Changes in environmental conditions which may arise quite independently of the project through natural processes should be noted. These represent the 'do-nothing' option. Major development projects have a long lead time. In this period, significant changes can occur in the existing conditions surrounding the site as a result of other development activity. Such changes need to be anticipated and taken into account in baseline descriptions.

5.14 Where aspects of the environment are subject to change, the baseline study should include reference to the nature of these trends and how they could affect the impacts of the proposed development. For example, the emission standards for the proposed development may be more demanding by the time the project is commissioned. Similarly, recent and proposed development in an area may be taking up the capacity of existing foul drainage facilities. Further development may lead to overloading and possible water pollution.

TABLE 8: Subject Matter to be Considered in Drafting the Project Description

Nature and Purpose of the Development

- Function of the proposal, with economic and operational context
- Alternatives considered (if appropriate)

Characteristics of the Proposed Site

- Location; Size; Summary of topography, landscape & natural or manmade features

---

Characteristics of the Proposed Development

- Size; Site layout ; Shape ; Character ; Landscape proposals (including grading) ;
- Car parking ; Entrances and exits ; Access to public transport ;
- Provision for pedestrians and cyclists ; Provision for utilities
- Any other relevant information (including emissions to air, water and land)

Phasing of the Development

- Construction phase
- Nature and phasing of construction ; Frequency, duration and location of intrusive operations
- Timing, location and extent of mitigation measures ; Use and transport of raw materials ;
- Number of workers or visitors
- Operational phase
- Processes, raw materials ; Emissions (air, water, noise, vibration, lighting etc)
- Number of employees or other users ; Traffic generation
- Likely expansion or secondary development
- To be covered so far as the effects of such development can be anticipated at the time the ES is prepared.
- Decommissioning/Closure Stages

Chapter 6 POLICIES AND PLANS

Statutory plans - National and International policies - Development Plans - Government Standards and Guidelines

STATUTORY PLANS

6.1 An ES should include a section on policies and plans which are relevant to the environmental assessment of the development in question. The objective is to demonstrate how these policy guidelines have been taken into account in developing the project and compiling the ES, and to provide a picture of the decision making context in which the environmental impacts will be evaluated. Discussion of these issues should focus on areas of environmental concern which have been highlighted in the scoping and consultation process or revealed in the course of the baseline surveys.

NATIONAL AND INTERNATIONAL POLICIES

6.2 Environmental policies operate at international, national, regional and local levels. The ES should demonstrate awareness of the implications of these policies for development proposals. International level policies may be contained in EC Directives or International Conventions. At the national level, statements of Government policy such as Planning Policy Guidance Notes[1], Minerals Planning Guidance Notes, Environment White Papers, the UK Sustainable Development Strategy and Government Circulars may be relevant. Advice issued by environmental authorities, such as English Nature, Scottish Natural Heritage, Cadw etc may also need to be considered. At the regional level, Regional Planning Guidance should be referred to.

DEVELOPMENT PLANS[2]

6.3 At the county and district level, development plan policies should be referred to in the context of the particular development proposal. Planning authorities are now required to determine planning applications in accordance with the development plan for the area, unless material considerations indicate otherwise. The development plan must take environmental considerations into account. It will also contain policy on appropriate land uses and conditions which must be met before certain developments are approved.

[1] In Scotland, planning policy guidance is issued in a different form. It comprises National Planning Policy Guidelines, circulars and Planning Advice Notes.

[2] In Scotland the development plan comprises the structure plan, prepared by Regional and Islands Councils, and the local plan prepared by the District Councils. Borders, Dumfries and Galloway and Highland Regional Councils also prepare local plans within their areas. Following re-organsiation in 1996, new unitary authorities will prepare both structure and local plans. In some areas, authorities will produce joint structure plans.

6.4 If the ES acknowledges the importance of development plans and explains how policies have been taken into account it is more likely to be accepted as an objective and credible analysis. It is important, however, that references to plans should concentrate on key issues and avoid unnecessary repetition.

6.5 In a non-metropolitan area the development plan comprises the county's structure plan, minerals and waste local plans, and the district's local plan. In metropolitan areas there are only unitary development plans. In preparing an ES, developers should give serious consideration to ways in which their proposals can be designed to accommodate policy objectives as outlined in the plans' strategic framework. The status of the plan in question, ie the stage it has reached in the process, should also be noted. Additional documents such as committee reports and reports of survey may provide a useful indication of a local authority's most recent position.

GOVERNMENT STANDARDS AND GUIDELINES

6.6 It may also be appropriate in the ES's section on policies and plans, to refer to government standards or guidelines which would affect various aspects of the project's construction and final operation. These might include, for example, air quality guidelines and limits, occupational and environmental noise limits, water quality standards and pollution emission levels.

Chapter 7 PREDICTION AND EVALUATION OF IMPACTS

Potential and predicted impacts - their nature and magnitude - evaluation of impacts - mitigation.

7.1 It is helpful if each environmental topic is discussed in the ES in a logical sequence distinguishing between:

- potential impacts;
- the existing baseline conditions;
- predicted impacts, giving a measure of their nature, extent and magnitude;
- the scope for mitigating adverse effects; and,
- a statement evaluating the significance of unavoidable impacts.

7.2 Impacts should be predicted for each of the stages of development, including site preparation, construction and commissioning, operation, decommissioning and site restoration, as appropriate. Distinctions should be drawn according to the timing, duration and location of the predicted impacts. Attention should also be paid to impacts which may result from accidents or unplanned events. The methodology used to predict these impacts should be stated and any gaps in data or analysis described. It will assist planning authorities in reaching a decision if the data sampling techniques and methods of measurement, and analysis on which predictions are based can be readily understood by non-experts and others involved

POTENTIAL AND PREDICTED IMPACTS

7.3 One of the difficulties in balancing the weight to be given to different sections of an ES arises in deciding what emphasis should be given to potential and predicted impacts. An ES may be criticised for lack of objectivity if it over-emphasises the positive impacts or suggests that every potential adverse impact can be resolved by the application of mitigating measures. But equally open to criticism would be placing too much emphasis on potential adverse impacts which are ultimately capable of being overcome. The following examples, based on dust generation from a proposed quarry extension, gives an example of contrasting ways of describing potential and predicted impacts.

7.4 A poorly prepared statement is shown in **Table 9**.

TABLE 9: A Poorly Prepared Statement

Air and Climate:
• Quarrying can cause dust, but due to the direction of the prevailing winds, and the measures to be taken to suppress dust at source, including use of water spraying and cessation of operations in high winds, any dust leaving the site will be minimal. There will be no significant impact.

7.5 A well prepared statement might cover the same topic more precisely and objectively (**Table 10**).

NATURE AND MAGNITUDE OF IMPACTS

7.6 The nature of both potential and predicted impacts needs to be described in simple and unambiguous language so that it is clear what issues are being addressed. The description should be kept as concise as possible and identify:

- the source and/or cause of the potential problem;
- the receptor of the impact;
- the way in which the effect is transmitted from source to receptor; and
- the potential consequences.

7.7 The magnitude of the predicted impact is likely to be a combined measure of the total extent of the area affected and the scale of the effects. Where possible the effect of the impact should be quantified.

EVALUATION OF PREDICTED IMPACTS

7.8 Evaluating the significance of effects requires a statement distinct from the preceding analysis. The conclusions on significance are essentially a matter of judgement. These conclusions will not automatically be accepted or upheld by the planning authority or the general public, especially where judgements about degrees of nuisance or unquantifiable aspects are concerned. In the example in Tables 9 and 10, there may be general agreement about the pattern of dust dispersal and the approximate volume in given areas. But those most directly affected may dispute its significance in terms of annoyance.

TABLE 10: A Well Prepared Statement

Air and Climate:

- **Potential impacts:** Mineral extraction is a process which cannot be undertaken without creating some dust and this has the potential to cause localised air pollution. Dust is generated when rock is blasted , excavated, and crushed, and also when contractor's plant travel over internal roads. Fine particles may also be lifted from exposed surfaces by wind. The nature of the particles varies with the source material. Hard rock quarrying, such as at Sourbeck may give rise to angular , dense fragments which settle close to the point of origin, while excavation of chalk and other softer rocks produce lighter finer particles which may be blown considerable distances.

- **Baseline Survey:** A one month survey was undertaken in August around the active workings and the proposed extension to Sourbeck quarry using equipment and analysis procedures laid down in BS 1747 part 5; 1972; confirmed January 1986 (Methods for the Measurement of Air Pollution, part 5 Directional Gauges).

- Results recorded at 4 of the 5 reading stations locate within 200 metres of the active workings show 10 day percentage obscuration values ranging between 5 and 20.5. results from the 5 stations surrounding the proposed extension ranged from 0.9 to 11.

- **Analysis:** Dust deposition varies considerably in both rural and urban areas depending upon weather conditions and types of activity taking place. The wide range of values at Sourbeck is therefore to be expected. However, the higher levels of deposition around the active workings by comparison with the ambient levels in the open countryside around the proposed extension confirms that quarrying activity does contribute to increased dust levels locally.

- **Predicted Impacts:** Based on the author's professional judgement, there are no reasons for assuming that the method of working in the proposed extension will give rise to higher levels of dust operation than those which currently occur., although the area of land affected will extend an equivalent distance beyond the boundary of the new working area. Dust generated by the workings is non-toxic and discussions with local farmers and MAFF officers have confirmed that existing levels of dust deposition have had no observable effects on crop yields.

- Two cottages located 200 metres to the east of the quarry may experience a marginal increase in dust deposition under exceptional weather conditions, but the effects will be very slight and of no environmental significance.

- **Mitigation:** Regular monitoring will be carried out around the quarry extension and the results will be assessed by staff of the Broughton laboratory physics department. Strict controls will be exercised over blasting operations which will not take place when wind speeds exceed 22 knots. Haul roads within the quarry will be sprayed continuously in drought conditions.

- **Statement of Significance:** Some dust will be generated by the extension. This will not exceed present levels, although the area affected will be enlarged. Informed local opinion confirms that dust will have no effect on crops and livestock. On one or two days in the year, dust may reach two cottages occupied by quarry workers. Staff at Broughton Laboratory have confirmed that no risk to health is involved but minor nuisance may be caused.

7.9 One approach to the evaluation of impacts is to assess the geographical level of importance of the issues under consideration in terms of environmental and planning policy guidelines. For example:

- an impact of **international** importance would be one which affects an interest of international concern such as a wetlands site protected under the Ramsar convention, a special protection area for birds or the discharge of pollutants into the atmosphere or the sea;

- an impact of **national importance** would be one which affects the national interest as identified by Government policies such as the effects of a development on a National Park, AONB, SSSI or a Grade 1 listed building;

- impacts of **regional or county-wide** importance would include those where the scale of impact is such that it could support or undermine regional guidance or Structure Plan policy, such as the erosion of a green belt or destruction of a Regionally Important Geological Site;

- impacts of **district-wide** importance will be of relevance within the context of the planning authority's administrative boundary; and

- impacts of **local** or localised importance will be those which affect a limited area, or are largely contained within the site itself, such as noise or dust emissions, traffic nuisance, visual impact.

7.10 Having defined the geographical level of importance of the subject matter, it is then appropriate to consider whether the predicted environmental impacts have any significant effects. A distinction should be made between major, minor or no significant effects and whether the impact is adverse or beneficial. Significance may also be assessed by examining the sensitivity and rarity of the environment in question.

7.11 In addition to comments on importance and significance it is sometimes helpful to describe the **nature** of impacts in more detail. As well as being adverse or beneficial, they may also be categorised as short or long term, permanent or temporary, irreversible or reversible, and direct or indirect.

7.12 It is also important when describing potential or predicted impacts to distinguish between events which are **unavoidable and those which are uncertain,** including those which are unlikely to happen. Information about the level of confidence in a given prediction should be included in the ES.

7.13 It may be helpful for the purpose of the non-technical summary (see **paragraph 4.21**) to provide an overall summary table which records the relative weights attached to the significance of individual impacts; an example is given in **Figure 2.**

FIGURE 2: Example of ES Summary Table Showing Relative Weights Given to Significance of Impacts (Note: Only a selection of key issues is given.)

Topic area	Description of impact	Geographical level of Importance of Issue					Impact	Nature	Significance
		I	N	R	D	L			
Human Beings	Disturbance to existing properties from traffic & noise				*		Adverse	St, R	Major
	Coalescence of existing settlements			*			Adverse	Lt, IR	Major
Flora & Fauna	Loss of grassland of local nature conservation value					*	Adverse	Lt, IR	Minor
	Creation of new habitats					*	Beneficial	Lt, R	Minor
	Increased recreation pressure on SSSI		*				Adverse	Lt, R	Minor
Soil & Geology	Loss of 300 acres agricultural soils (grade 3B)			*			Adverse	Lt, IR	Minor
Water	Increased rates of surface water run-off				*		Adverse	Lt, IR	Minor
	Reduction in groundwater recharge			*			Adverse	Lt, R	Minor

KEY:

I = International
N = National
R = Regional
D = District
L = Local

St = Short term
Lt = Long term
R = Reversible
IR = Irreversible

MITIGATION OF ADVERSE EFFECTS

7.14 The ES should include a section outlining opportunities for reducing identified negative environmental impacts by mitigating or compensating for adverse effects, or by enhancing beneficial aspects of the development.

7.15 Mitigation measures should be identified, indicating the developer's commitment to their implementation together with any further impacts that they may create. Although it is not a legal requirement, the developer may find it helpful to explain any non-mitigation of a predicted adverse impact. The ES should also describe the nature, extent and location of any compensation or enhancement measures which would result in environmental improvements not necessarily related to a specifically identified environmental impact.

7.16 The scope for improving the quality of the development and reducing potential adverse effects on the environment during the design process is one of the benefits of EA. However, the mitigating measures may themselves sometimes have potentially adverse aspects which should also be recognised. For example, earth-moulding to provide noise baffles or screening can create unnatural landforms which can be visually intrusive. New habitats or open areas to compensate for damage to existing plants or recreation areas also need to be assessed in their own right for example, tree screening could disturb other natural habitats.

APPENDICES

Appendix

1

HUMAN BEINGS

1. The way impacts of a project on the physical environment affect human beings needs to be described in Environmental Statements and this appendix deals with concerns relating to population, and housing and services.

2. In practice, the assessment of the potential impacts of a project on human beings represents a distillation of many of the topics covered in other sections of an Environmental Assessment. For instance, the full analysis of air pollution will need to consider the implications for human health and welfare, as will a full analysis of water quality. The section on human beings should, therefore, be cross-referenced with those impacts identified in other topic areas which appear likely to have an impact on human well-being. It may also need to consider, if relevant to the development in question, topics such as the environmental consequences of changes in population, housing and services, or the implications of noise and traffic on human well-being.

3. The **scoping** process should consider which environmental effects, if any, are likely to affect human beings. It should consider the range of subject matter and the level of investigation required keeping a balance between broad generalisations and fine definitions. **Table 11** overleaf summarises possible impacts on humans.

POPULATION

4. Many development proposals will have little or no impacts on population. An impact is most likely to occur where **major development** is proposed in a relatively remote and lightly populated area. In such cases benefit may flow from the stemming of outward migration and the support of the local economy and services. However, inward migration may lead to conflicts of interest between the incomers and established resident population or where a new development requires skills not locally available, leading to a migration inwards of suitably skilled staff.

5. **Potential impacts:** In a few major cases, for example the construction of a reservoir, the proposal may involve the involuntary relocation of communities or individual households. More often, a major development will result in the movement of people through choice. Two factors influence the significance of the effects. The

first is the relative scale of migration in relation to existing population levels; the second is the timescale over which it takes place.

6. At its most basic level, a rapid increase in population may overload the capacity of existing services (water, gas, electricity and sewerage), and transport and education facilities, as well as increase pressures on housing stock and the demand for land.

TABLE 11: Possible Impacts on Human Beings Relating to Population, Housing and Services

Effect on Humans	Potential Environment Effect
• Population:	
Changes in Population structure	Changes in demand for housing, services and recreation facilities
Increase in inward migration	Increases in demand for housing, services and recreation facilities
Increase in outward migration	Possible changes in use and management of rural areas, increases in numbers of redundant buildings, possible declining environmental quality
• Housing:	
Requirement for temporary accommodation during construction	Raises issues of location, design and siting.
Increase in demand for permanent housing	If existing housing stock is underused, spare capacity is taken up. If fully used, the pressure may lead to problems of overcrowding, long distance commuting etc and to a demand for new dwellings. This may require additional land allocations.
• Services:	
Increase in demand for hospitals, schools, shops recreation facilities etc.	Any surplus is taken up. Where there is no surplus, difficulties of overcrowding of existing facilities and reduced standards in services (for instance a fall in river water quality as a consequence of increases in foul water drainage) will lead to a demand for extra provision. This in turn may require additional land allocations. Increasing demands placed on infrastructure and utilities.

7. **Baseline Surveys:** In order to assess population impacts, baseline information should describe the characteristics of the local population in terms of age, sex and marital status. Where **significant** migration inwards is anticipated, data on housing provision, schools, hospitals etc. and their use may need to be collected.

8. An indication of the extent of migration to the area around a proposed major development may be gained by considering the proportion of new jobs (including those in suppliers etc.) which will be filled by local people and the proportion which must be made up from outside the area.

9. The timing and nature of the immigration will be important. The initial round of migration will be associated with the construction phase of a development, and may comprise a high proportion of young, single males who make relatively light demands on education, health or recreation facilities, and may be housed in temporary accommodation on or near site. This migration will be of a short term nature. A second phase of migration comprising those people directly employed in the development may take place when the development's final use commences, and is likely to include a higher proportion of family groups. A third phase of migration is less well defined and is harder to predict, comprising people who are moving to find work in the ancillary industries and expanding local companies which are supported by the new development.

10. **Determining magnitude and significance:** comparison of the employment created by a proposed development with the characteristics of the local labour market should have established whether migration inwards is likely to occur. An age-sex-marital analysis of expected migrants will give an estimate of the likely demand for housing, educational, health and recreational provision. Comparison with existing and planned provision will indicate the likelihood of significant environmental effects.

11. Any significant socio-economic differences between the existing and migrating populations should be noted, since such differences result in impacts on the local culture (for example the influx of non-Welsh speakers into a Welsh speaking rural area).

12. **Sources of Information:** Analysis of the likely impact of a proposed development on population will require demographic information for the area concerned. Census data may be obtained from the **Office of Population and Census Surveys,** although the local authority may well have a range of more up-to date and detailed information.

13. There are no specific guidelines for assessing the effects of major development on population, although there are standard procedures, including shift/share analysis, for examining population trends and projecting future change. These statistical and demographic techniques are employed in the estimation of future population levels for local authority plans. Detailed studies of population trends are only

likely to be required for very large projects where specialist advice should be obtained.

HOUSING AND SERVICES

14. The demand for new housing and additional services may be a subsidiary issue to major development proposals. Where the scale of such ancillary development can easily be absorbed within the existing housing structure, or imposes no significant increased loads on existing services, it would be sufficient to note this briefly in the ES. There may, however, be circumstances in which new housing and essential services are themselves likely to create significant impacts on the environment, in which case a full assessment of the implications will be required. At the other extreme, the taking up of vacant housing and the support of under-used local services can be a positive benefit.

15. **Potential Impacts:** Where the scale of housing demand is likely to exceed the capacity of the existing housing stock or allocated reserves of land, consideration should be given, as part of the development proposal, to ways of resolving the potential difficulties which might otherwise occur. The living environment created for new residents and the effects which new communities may have on existing settlements should also be considered. Services, including public utilities and transport, may have a major role to play in supporting new development and should not be overlooked.

16. **Baseline Surveys:** Demand for housing and services likely to be generated by the proposed development, will need to be identified and compared with data on the range and type of property and development land available within the project area. Population statistics, information on trends in the size of household units and other socio-economic indicators may also need to be consulted.

17. **Prediction and Mitigation of Impacts:** The primary purpose in assessing demand for housing and services is to ensure that the new development can be assimilated into the area with maximum benefit to the existing community and minimal adverse impact. It should be done in ways which optimise the environmental quality of any new or expanded settlement. It is primarily the consequences of rapid or unplanned change which have direct and adverse impacts on human beings.

18. **Employment:** Creation of substantial new employment may be the catalyst for changes in population and housing, and the demand for services and natural resources, with consequent effects on the physical environment. Analysis of the existing employment structure and local economy may therefore be appropriate in providing background information for the ES.

19. **Sources of Information:** Information on existing housing stock and future building programmes will usually be available from the local authority planning

and housing departments, as well as from housing associations, estate agents and others. The particular needs for services should be known to the local authority and utility undertakers.

Appendix

2

NOISE AND VIBRATION

1. Noise can have a significant effect on the environment and on the quality of life enjoyed by individuals and communities.

2. Determining the likely impact of noise resulting from development is complex and requires specialist skills. The nature of the subject is such that there is no precisely correct way of approaching the assessment procedure, and the guidelines and standards used in the assessment will vary from project to project. It is strongly recommended therefore that the noise impact assessment, where this is necessary, is carried out by staff or agencies with the expertise to measure and predict noise and interpret the data. This appendix offers only a broad outline of the issues involved.

3. Noise has been defined as 'sound which is undesired by the recipient'. The perception of noise may be reflected by many factors (acoustic and non-acoustic) but in general the impact in response to a noise depends on the level of noise, the margin by which it exceeds the background level, its spectral character, and temporal variation. In some cases other factors such as the time of day, day of the week, duration, and other acoustic features such as tonality and impulsiveness will be important. Any assessment of noise must take account not only of the level of noise but also of these other factors.

4. Vibrations, even very low magnitude, may be perceptible to people and can interfere with the satisfactory conduct of certain activities, eg delicate procedures in hospital operating theatres, use of very sensitive laboratory equipment etc. Vibration nuisance is frequently associated with the assumption that if vibration can be felt, then damage is inevitable. However, considerably greater levels of vibration are required to cause damage to building structures (see for example British Standard BS 7385) or to cause computers and other similar electronic equipment to malfunction.

POTENTIAL IMPACTS

5. There are many effects caused by noise. It can cause annoyance, interfere with communication, cause fatigue, increase heart rate, reduce sleep quality and sense of well-being. In some cases it can lead to loss of amenity.

6. Noisy development may also have an effect on the welfare of livestock and on wildlife. For information of the effects on livestock, developers should contact the Ministry of Agriculture Fisheries and Food (Land Use Planning Unit).

Potential sources of noise and vibration

7. There are four main types of noise pollution :

- **Industrial noise**: includes factories, industrial plant, manufacturing, infrastructure projects, industrial sources in commercial premises, construction, quarries etc. ;

- **Transportation noise**: includes that from road traffic, railways, aircraft and water borne craft;

- **Leisure noise**: includes that from motor sports, sporting events, leisure centres, pubs etc; and,

- **Domestic noise**: includes music, intruder alarms and parties. In general it will not be necessary to include this type of noise in an environmental assessment.

8. Potential sources of vibration include blasting in quarries, mines, construction or demolition, piling in construction, dynamic soil compaction, rail and road traffic, and heavy machinery .

9. Vibrations transmitted from site activities to the neighbourhood may therefore cause anxiety as well as annoyance, can disturb sleep, work or leisure activities. As with noise, in any neighbourhood some individuals will be more sensitive than others.

10. Damage to buildings arising from vibration may be classified as :

- **Cosmetic**: the formation of hairline cracks on drywall surfaces, or the growth of existing cracks in plaster or drywall surfaces;

- **Minor**: the formation of large cracks or loosening and falling of plaster or drywall surfaces, or cracks through bricks/concrete blocks;

- **Major**: damage to structural elements of the building, cracks in support columns, loosening of joints, splaying of masonry cracks etc.

PREDICTION AND MEASUREMENT OF NOISE

11. The human ear detects sound which lies in the 20 to 16,000 Hertz (Hz) frequency range. However, sensitivity is greatest within the 500 - 5000 Hz range. This

characteristic is reflected in the way sound is measured and also suggests that attention is paid to sources of noise which lie within these ranges.

12. Sound can be measured either in terms of its generation or in terms of its reception. The former measures in terms of energy needed to generate it; the latter measures the pressure that is exerted on a membrane by the sound waves, expressed as sound pressure levels. This is the more commonly used measure.

13. The basic unit used in noise measurement is the decibel (dB). This is an objective measure of sound pressure and does not therefore measure loudness as sensed by the human ear. To take account of this, the decibel measure is corrected by the 'A' weighting factor. The resultant unit of loudness is termed dB(A).

14. Various noise measurement indices exist to describe noise sources with differing characteristics. The $L_{A90,T}$ index indicates dB(A) levels that are exceeded for 90% of the specified measurement time period. This is currently used in the measurement of background noise (see BS 4142). $L_{A10,T}$ represents noise levels exceeded for 10% of a given time interval. This is used in the measurement of road traffic noise. An alternative measure is L_{AeqT} which represents the average continuous sound level over a period of time. This is the principal measurement index for environmental noise (see BS 7445, ISO 1996).

Vibration

15. In general, building vibration should be measured in acceleration terms. In some cases, such as impulsive events, it may be found convenient to measure in terms of particle velocity so that peak values may be identified. The peak particle velocity (ppv) is the simplest indicator of both perceptibility and the risk of damage to structures. The vibration dose value is recommended in British Standard BS 6472 as the appropriate measure of nuisance from vibration.

16. Peak particle velocity is the instantaneous maximum velocity reached by the vibrating elements as it oscillates about its rest position. In order to obtain a typical value of ppv it will be necessary to monitor a representative number of cycles of operation.

NOISE STANDARDS AND REGULATIONS

17. Planning Policy Guidance Note PPG 24, Planning and Noise, offers advice on how the planning system can be used to minimise the adverse impact of noise without placing unreasonable restrictions on development or adding unduly to the costs and administrative burdens on developers. The guidance outlines the considerations to be taken into account in determining planning applications for developments which will generate noise and also for noise sensitive developments. The following paragraphs, which deal with some project areas which commonly attract environmental assessment, summarise guidance relating

to the assessment of noise from different sources published in PPG 24.

Noise from industrial and commercial developments

18. The likelihood of complaints about noise from industrial development can be assessed, where the Standard is relevant, using guidance in BS4142:1990. Tonal or impulsive characteristics of the noise are likely to increase the scope for complaints and this is taken into account by the "rating level" defined in BS 4142. This rating level is used by the planning authority when stipulating the level of noise that can be permitted. The likelihood of complaints is indicated by the difference between the noise from the new development (expressed in terms of the rating level) and the existing background noise. The standard states that a difference of 10dB or higher indicates that complaints are likely. A difference of around 5dB is of marginal significance.

19. Since background noise levels vary throughout a 24 hour period, it will be necessary to assess the acceptability of noise levels for separate periods (day and night) chosen to match the hours of operation of the proposed development. General guidance on noise levels within buildings is to be found in BS 8233:1987. Guidance on the control of noise from surface mineral workings can be found in MPG11.

Noise from Construction sites

20. Guidance on assessing noise from construction sites may be found in British Standard BS 5228, parts 1 - 4. In particular Part 1:1984, "Code of Practice for basic information and procedures for noise control" should be useful; as well as providing general information it describes a method for predicting noise from construction sites.

Noise from Landfill Waste Disposal Sites

21. The main source of noise on these sites is from vehicle movements, tipping operations and site plant. Useful information of predicting the noise can be found in BS 5228 :part 1 :1984. Conditions attached to waste disposal installations by planning authorities generally place limits on the amount of waste, frequency of deliveries and hours of operation. These will have an effect of the amount of noise generated but site licence conditions can also relate to noise control specifically.

Noise from road, rail and air traffic

22. Some guidance and information about a means of calculating noise resulting from road traffic is available in the Calculation of Road Traffic Noise (Department of Transport / Welsh Office, 1988), and the Memorandum on the Noise Insulation (Scotland) Regulations 1975. Advice and information is also available in "Design

Manual for Roads and Bridges" Vol 11, section 3, part 7 -traffic noise and vibration. The Department of Transport has recently produced similar guidance on the calculation of noise from railways, Calculation of Railway Noise 1995.

23. The Department of Transport expresses aircraft noise exposure contours in terms of L_{eq} dB(A) over the period 07.00 hours to 23.00 hours. This index is equivalent to an L_{Aeq16h} dB. Using forecast contours, it should be possible to determine approximately which areas are likely to fall within the different noise categories described in PPG 24. Technical advice on the production of noise contours can be obtained from the Department of Safety, Environment and Engineering, Civil Aviation Authority, 45-49 Kingsway, Holborn, London WC2B 6TE.

Vibration

24. British Standard BS 6472 offers guidance on the evaluation of human exposure to vibration in buildings and British Standard BS 7385 covers the measurement and evaluation of vibration in buildings and damage levels from ground borne vibration.

ASSESSMENT OF NOISE AND VIBRATION

Noise

25. A number of assessment locations will need to be identified for each project. The actual number of identified assessment locations will vary from project to project depending on factors such as the predicted level of intruding noise, likely variations in the level of intruding noise, local topography and local climatic conditions. The distribution of the assessment locations should cover all noise sensitive premises.

26. Noise sensitive premises include any occupied premises used as a dwelling (including gardens), educational establishment or hospital. Special consideration should also be given to development which would affect the quiet enjoyment of National Parks, the Broads, AONB or Heritage Coasts.

27. At each of the identified assessment locations both the existing noise levels and the predicted noise levels occurring as result of the development will have to be determined. These levels may be obtained by measurement and/or calculation.

Vibration

28. Similarly, a number of vibration assessment locations will need to be identified for each project (these may well be different from the noise location). The number of locations will vary from project to project depending upon factors such as the proposed source and distance from other development, topography and geology. The predicted impact vibration levels may in some circumstances be obtained by

a number of small test explosions or vibrations designed to replicate the characteristic of the vibration emanating from the development.

29. **Scoping:** Close examination of the project proposal must identify all significant actual and potential sources of noise and vibration such as local industrial and transportation sources.

30. Scoping should also identify the likely recipients of any noise impacts. These should include noise sensitive premises. The identification of these potential recipients will help focus the baseline survey to those nose sensitive locations where impacts are likely to be most significant.

31. **Baseline Surveys:** The baseline survey should be tailored to reflect the types of noise and vibration impacts identified by the scoping process.

32. **Prediction of Impacts:** The prediction (which may in certain circumstances be based on actual measurement) of likely noise and vibration impacts should build upon the work undertaken during the scoping and baseline stages of assessment. The project may require separate predictions for its various constituent phases. These may include, for example, site reclamation, construction, use and decommissioning.

33. **Determining the significance of impacts** : When placing a value on the predicted impacts, the environmental assessment study will have to rate the significance of the impacts in terms of factors such as the number of people affected, magnitude of impact and time scale of impact.

34. **Mitigation of impacts:** Where impacts are considered significant, measures can be introduced control the source of, or reduce exposure to, noise and vibration. Examples of mitigation measures include:

    - **Design/engineering:** reducing noise at source by, for example, using quieter machines; use of acoustic enclosures, improving the sound insulation and vibration isolation

    - **Lay-out:** ensuring an adequate distance between the point of source and recipient; making use of natural contours and barriers; and

    - **Administrative:** limiting operating time of the source of noise.

Selected Sources of Further Information

- British Standard 5228: 1984 (parts 1-3), 1992 (part 4), Noise control on construction and open sites
- British Standard 5821: 1984, Rating the sound insulation in buildings and of building elements
- British Standard 8233: 1987, Sound insulation and noise reduction for buildings.
- British Standard 4142: 1990, Method for rating industrial noise affecting mixed residential and industrial areas.
- British Standard 7445: 1991, Description and measurement of environmental noise.
- British Standard 6472: 1992, Guide to evaluation of human exposure to vibration in buildings (1Hz to 80Hz)
- DoE Circular 11/95 - The Use of Conditions in Planning Permissions (1995)
- Mineral Planning Guidance Note 11 - The Control of Noise at Surface Mineral Workings (1993) - HMSO
- Planning Policy Guidance Note 15 - Planning and the Historic Environment (1994) - HMSO
- Planning Policy Guidance Note 17 - Sport and Recreation (1991) - HMSO
- Planning Policy Guidance Note 23 - Planning and Pollution Control (1994) - HMSO
- Planning Policy Guidance Note 24 - Planning and Noise (1994) - HMSO
- Report of Noise Review Working Party, 1990 (HMSO) (ISBN 0 11 752343 7)

TRAFFIC AND TRANSPORT

1. This appendix is concerned specifically with the environmental impacts of traffic associated with new developments rather than with the impacts of new road construction and use of new roads. It is unlikely that the entire range of impacts discussed below would occur except in the case of the largest development proposals.

POTENTIAL IMPACTS

2. Traffic associated with a new development can have a wide range of often adverse environmental effects. These vary in their extent and significance according to the type, location and size of the development in question, and the composition of associated traffic. The impacts may also vary during construction and operational phases and this should be reflected in the ES.

3. Increases in traffic flows can lead to increases in **noise** and **vibration** in the vicinity of existing or new roads (as discussed in Appendix 2).

4. An area of continued and growing concern is the **air pollution** caused by traffic. (See also Appendix 8). Any increase in traffic flows in the vicinity of a development will lead to increases in local concentrations of pollutants such as carbon monoxide, sulphur dioxide, oxides of nitrogen, particulates and lead. The level of air pollution is influenced by traffic flow, vehicle speed, vehicle type and engine efficiency. Air pollution from vehicles may be particularly important where roads pass through, or close to residential areas, schools or recreation areas, or from the stop-start characteristics of traffic at junctions. If the additional traffic generated by a development takes traffic flows beyond the capacity of the local road network, the resulting congestion may lead to a disproportionate local increase in pollution. Other airborne pollutants include dust and dirt deposited alongside roads and carbon dioxide which causes enhanced global warming (traffic accounts for 19% of UK carbon dioxide emissions).

5. Traffic may also constitute a **visual impact**, particularly where heavy goods vehicles are present, or where increased traffic flows are introduced into an area of high landscape or townscape value. Increased vehicle flows or vehicle speeds can result

in an increase in **pedestrian delay**, making crossing difficult. Similarly, increases in vehicle traffic flow may result in an increase in **danger** to pedestrians, cyclists and motorists. Such delays and increased level of risk can contribute to an increase in **severance**, i.e. the suppression or diversion of trips.

TRAVEL AND TRAFFIC

6. In assessing the impact of new developments, consideration should be given to the impact of travel likely to be generated. This includes both the effects of the whole journey (including the frequency, length, timing and mode of travel) and the impact on the local transport network at critical times. The volume and type of traffic generated by a new development is a function of its accessibility. This in turn is determined by its location, nature and size.

7. The Government's policy on transport and planning in England is set out in Planning Policy Guidance Note 13 - 'Transport'. This advises local authorities to implement policies and proposals in their development plans which will reduce the need to travel, reduce reliance on the private car and encourage other means of travel which have less environmental impact. Plans should guide development to locations where the travel generated will be minimised. Plans should also include complementary policies setting out proposals for traffic calming, reduced car parking requirements and better facilities for pedestrians and cyclists.

8. The accessability of any given development will be largely determined by its location. If a development is not easily accessible by walking, cycling or public transport, then a large proportion of trips to and from the site will be made by car. Similarly, freight movements will be mostly by road unless there is easy access from the site to the rail and/or waterway network. Where freight has to be moved by road in significant quantities, lorry vehicle movements will have an impact unless the development is located within easy access to the trunk road network.

9. The nature of the development is also important. For example, warehousing and some types of manufacturing generally do not attract many journeys by car but will involve quite high freight movement. On the other hand, offices, shops and leisure developments attract many individual visitors but have relatively low freight requirements. The time of traffic movements may also be a consideration. Night time journeys may be more significant than a similar traffic flow earlier in the day.

10. The composition of large-scale development also influences traffic generation. Single-use development, such as employment or recreation facilities, is likely to induce distinct peaks of traffic flow. Mixed-use schemes may reduce traffic as people can use the same journey for several different purposes. Further, mixed-use development can help spread trips more evenly throughout the day, thus reducing peak flows during morning and evening rush hours when adverse

conditions on the local road and public transport networks are likely to be most significant.

MEASURING AND PREDICTING TRAFFIC FLOWS

Measurement

11. An assessment of traffic impacts requires a description of the current transport network and any foreseeable changes. The local authority may hold extensive data describing existing traffic patterns. This could help determine whether traffic levels vary by time of year, or whether recognisable trends in traffic flows exist. The review of existing traffic data will identify areas where further measurement or estimation is required, perhaps of total or classified vehicle counts on sections of roads or at junctions, and to differentiate between different times of day etc.

Predicting traffic associated with new developments

12. Prediction of future traffic flows comprises two main elements: the calculation of trip generation, and the assignment of this traffic between different routes.

13. Typical trip generation forecasts are statistically derived from characteristics such as size, number of employees, location and type. Various technical guides exist to assist with these calculations (for example, information may be found in the Institute of Highways and Transportation guidelines for Traffic Impact Assessment 1994, the Department of Transport's Traffic Appraisal Manual (TAM) and National Road Traffic Forecasts (NRTF) and the Scottish Development Department's report Traffic Impact of Developments in Scotland 1989). In addition, a number of databases contain trip generation information for a range of actual developments, for example the TRICS database, developed by county authorities in the South East. The method used in the calculations should be outlined in the ES.

14. The assignment of the predicted traffic between routes in the area is calculated with reference to the likely origins and destinations of employees, visitors and goods vehicles, together with the known characteristics of the local road network and any foreseeable changes. It is common practice to predict what will be the impacts of the development in its opening year and 15 years after its opening year. The assumptions normally required by such calculations and the method used should be clearly stated.

ASSESSMENT OF THE IMPACT OF TRAFFIC ASSOCIATED WITH A NEW DEVELOPMENT

15. **Scoping**: The nature, size and location of a development proposal, together with the characteristics of its surroundings should dictate whether a detailed assessment of likely traffic impacts is required. The developer should therefore make early contact with the local authority to try to agree the details of the assessment.

16. For a small development, or one with few employees and little movement of raw materials or goods, it may be decided that the traffic impacts of the development do not warrant detailed appraisal. In the case of a larger development, traffic impacts may be concentrated in the vicinity of a single stretch of road or a junction. Very large developments may require a more detailed approach, examining the changes in vehicle flows on a network of roads within an area around the proposed development, and requiring an assessment of likely consequences in terms of noise, air pollution or other effects.

17. The scoping process should identify the nature and extent of existing traffic data which may be held by the local authority, the Department of Transport, the Welsh Office Highways Directorate or the Scottish Office Development Department - National Roads Directorate. It should also establish factors against which the significance of changes in traffic flows can be assessed. These may include sensitive land uses such as hospitals, schools, dwellings, areas of nature conservation / landscape value or recreation areas.

18. **Baseline Surveys:** The scoping process should have determined the areas of particular concern and identified the extent of existing information. The main function of the subsequent baseline survey is to provide a benchmark against which the effects of the development may be judged, so account should be taken of any features expected to affect traffic flows by the time the proposed development opens, together with any new roads, railways or other developments that are proposed. The degree of certainty regarding possible changes should be clearly stated.

19. **Prediction of Impacts:** The analysis of traffic generation and distribution should indicate the extent to which existing routes and junctions have the capacity to accommodate the forecast traffic growth, and may have indicated the need for management methods (such as traffic signals). During this analysis, attention should be paid both to the degree of change and to the absolute levels of traffic.

20. Having established the volume of the flows that represent existing traffic together with that from the new development, and having identified areas of particular concern, the environmental impacts of the traffic should be considered for the various phases of the development. These will vary according to the locality, but may include noise, vibration, local concentrations of air pollutants, visual intrusion, effects of dust and salt spray, road safety, severance, traffic congestion and possible remedies. They can affect local residents, employees, buildings and the natural environment. Any net increase in traffic will increase emissions of carbon dioxide.

21. **Mitigation of Impacts:** Where the assessment has indicated that significant adverse effects are likely, a range of measures may be employed to ameliorate or mitigate these impacts.

22. The most fundamental means of reducing traffic impacts associated with a proposed development include a reduction in size or the selection of an alternative site where the local road network is better able to accommodate the associated traffic without adverse effects or which is better served by public transport.

23. If it is established that a development's traffic generation is associated with the movement of employees, visitors and customers to and from the site by car, alternative methods of transport may be considered.

24. **Public transport** provision may be improved by negotiating with the relevant operators. Alternatively, if the development is of sufficient size, the developer may be prepared to operate services.

25. **Cycling** can be encouraged by a range of positive measures such as the provision of cycle paths and lanes, secure parking, and areas where cyclists can shower and change prior to work. Travel to work on **foot** can be encouraged by the provision of well designed and secure footpaths linking the development with surrounding housing or shopping areas, or with public transport facilities.

26. Mitigation of specific impacts on roads around a development may be achieved by careful design of **site layout**, in particular the number and location of **access** points. It may be possible to reduce likely adverse effects by **traffic management** or **traffic calming** measures on streets around the site so that traffic flows are restricted to routes capable of accommodating them without significant adverse impacts. But there are indications that measures such as road humps are less successful in reducing noise from commercial vehicles, especially heavy lorries. The arguments for and against concentrating or dispersing traffic flows will vary according to the development and its location.

27. If traffic noise is considered to be a significant adverse effect of a development, and it cannot be tackled at source (by limiting vehicle flows in particular locations), **noise barriers** or insulation such as **double glazing** may be appropriate.

28. The impacts associated with the movement of heavy goods vehicles to and from a site may be mitigated by agreeing the **routes** used by such vehicles, transferring freight to be carried by **rail** (or rail and road), **water** or even **pipeline**, or by agreeing that **smaller vehicles** will be used. Grants continue to be available from the Department of Transport and the Welsh Office to assist towards the capital cost of constructing rail (or inland waterway) freight facilities where these will result in the transfer of specific traffic from road to rail/inland waterway or the retention of such traffic by these two modes. Efforts should also be made to safeguard existing railhead and wharfage facilities.

Selected Sources of Further Information

- Design Manual for Roads and Bridges : Volume 10 : Environmental Assessment - published by HMSO
- Design Manual for Roads and Bridges : Volume 11 (Sections 1 and 5) - published by HMSO
- Guidelines for the Environmental Assessment of Road Traffic - published by the Institute of Environmental Assessment
- Guidelines on Traffic Impact Assessment - Institute of Highways and Transportation
- National Road Traffic Forecasts - published by Department of Transport
- Policy Planning Guidance Note 13 (Wales) - Highways consideration in Development Control (1988) - Welsh Office
- Policy Planning Guidance Note 13 - Transport - Department of the Environment (1994)
- Traffic Appraisal Manual - published by the Department of Transport
- Traffic Impact of Developments in Scotland (1989) - Scottish Development Department

LAND USE

1. This Appendix deals with the environmental effects which development can have on primary land uses which, broadly speaking, does not include the built environment. It does not cover the environmental effects that the development and intensification of existing primary land uses is capable of having on the environment. Such projects may need to be subjected, where appropriate, to EA in their own right.

TYPES OF LAND USE

2. Many different uses may need to be considered in relation to different types of development and their settings and locations, including agriculture, forestry, mineral extraction, waste treatment and disposal, and recreation. The impacts of development proposals upon urban and rural settlements and their inhabitants should also be recognised. Many of these impacts are discussed under the other topic chapters in this Guidance. In all cases the ES should give attention to Government policies applicable to the relevant land uses, and reference made to the implications of such policies.

Agriculture

3. In rural areas agriculture is usually the predominant land use and although there have been significant changes in emphasis in recent years, the protection of the best and most versatile of agricultural land, the appearance of the countryside, and stimulation of the rural economy remain essential. There will be significant overlaps between the assessment of agricultural land use as a topic, and issues relating to geology and soils, landscape and nature conservation but the subject is sufficiently important to analyse in its own right. Studies should cover the four following areas.

4. **Agricultural Land Quality:** Agricultural land in England and Wales is classified by the Ministry of Agriculture Fisheries and Food as the basis of the Agricultural Land Classification; in Scotland by the Macauley Land Use Research Institute. Maps are available which give a general indication of land quality in all areas. For a detailed assessment on an individual land holding, close investigation by a site survey is required.

5. The best quality agricultural land should be protected from development except where there are no reasonable alternative sites on land of a lower quality. In the case of minerals, development may also be acceptable on best and most versatile agricultural land where land is capable of being restored to its original quality. In some poorer areas even non-prime land may have local importance for maintaining viable agriculture in the area. Any ES for development affecting agricultural land should make reference to the implications of government policy and, where land of a high quality is affected, it should set out reasoned arguments for the choice of the proposed development site, the justification for the proposal, and the reason for the rejection of alternative sites. In the case of minerals and waste development, details of site working and reclamation are required to demonstrate the standard of restoration that is to be achieved. Selected publications giving information about Government policies on development involving agricultural land are given at the end of this appendix.

6. **The Rural Economy:** Farming is an important industry and the farming community has a vital role to play, not only in terms of food production but in managing and conserving the countryside. Major developments may adversely affect the livelihoods of those who are directly involved in working the land by either directly displacing individual farms or associated effects from adjacent developments. Also, development can have further repercussions on the agricultural economy of the surrounding areas through indirect effects on markets, and on machinery and feedstuff suppliers. Where part or the entire farm is required for development, the assessment may need to examine:

- the type of farming system;
- the commercial and technical viability of the holding at its existing and reduced size; and,
- the scope for restructuring the business through land acquisition or diversification.

7. **Access and Severance:** Development in rural areas can result in land being severed from the main body of the farm, adding to operating costs and reducing or removing the economic viability of the unit. In some parts of the country, historic patterns of tenure, or the need to move stock between summer and winter pastures has resulted in a highly fragmented pattern of landholding. Consequently the assessment should take into account the effect of the development on all aspects of the farm business and may need to take in a much larger land area than that directly affected by the proposed development.

8. **Land Drainage:** Most farmland in lowland Britain has been improved by underdrainage. Dislocation of arterial drains, alteration of groundwater levels through pumping and abstraction or the acceleration of surface water run-off (for example from road construction), may all have significant effects on land

drainage. Land drainage and flood defence improvement works which have deemed planning permission are subject to the Land Drainage Improvement Works (Assessment of Environmental Effects) Regulations 1988[1] (as amended).

Forestry

9. Forests and woodlands provide a number of environmental benefits including a landscape, nature conservation and human amenity. Where development that requires EA under the Planning Regulations is likely to have a direct effect on areas of woodland and forestry, careful study of the existing woodland and forest structure will be required, covering:

- the type of tree species present;
- yield classes;
- potential loss of timber production;
- possible impacts on remaining trees (through windblow);
- effects on future woodland and forestry management;
- impacts on habitats, wildlife and landscape.

Afforestation itself can sometimes have adverse environmental effects and the assessment of these is covered under separate EA Regulations.

Mineral Extraction

10. In areas where planning permission for mineral extraction has been granted, or where preferred areas of search for minerals have been confirmed in development plans, any major development which might sterilise minerals resources or have adverse effects on future production, should be carefully scrutinised. This will be necessary not only where buildings and plant are constructed on or above mineral-bearing land, but where new development is sited on a critical access route, or too close to the extraction and processing area to allow effective working without severe environmental and economic disbenefits.

11. Examples of the types of development which could give rise to future problems for mineral extraction include plants manufacturing food products or hygiene and medical supplies which require to be totally dust-free, and instrument makers and other manufacturing processes with very low tolerance of vibration. Consideration also needs to be given, in the case of major housing development proposals, to the potential effects of dust, traffic, noise and vibration from adjacent mineral extraction sites.

[1] In Scotland the Environmental Assessment (Scotland) Regulations 1988, part v

Waste Treatment and Disposal

12. The issues relevant to mineral extraction apply equally to development which may be proposed in close proximity to waste treatment and disposal facilities. In addition, where a development is proposed on or near a site presently or previously used for landfill purposes, thorough investigation will be required to assess any potentially adverse effects arising from ground contamination, differential settlement and the production and migration of landfill gases. All these technical constraints are capable of resolution but must initially receive the appropriate level of attention. Information about development on or around landfill sites may be found in Waste Management Paper no 27, Landfill Gas.

Recreation

13. The potential effects of major development on recreational use of land, air and water, varies greatly with the nature of the development, and the characteristics and location of the site. In areas which are environmentally sensitive, recreational issues may be one of the most significant matters to be dealt with in an EA.

14. The Countryside Commission guidance note '**Environmental Assessment - The Treatment of Landscape and Countryside Recreation Issues**' identifies major recreational resources including access routes, parks, carparks, common land and many others. It proposes a similar method of assessing impacts on recreation to that set out in this Guide.

ASSESSMENT OF LAND USE

15. **Scoping:** The scoping stage will be essential to assess which aspects of primary land use are affected by the development and the level of information required to be collected during baseline studies to allow a proper assessment of the development to be undertaken.

16. **Baseline Surveys:** The starting point for a description of how land is being used will be the land use designations contained within current development plans, including Mineral and Waste Disposal Plans. Discussions with relevant Government agencies may also be useful.

17. Additional information which may be required will depend on the nature of the development and prevailing land uses but might include, for example:

    Agriculture: a description of land quality, land ownership and tenure, and the nature of the farming enterprises. Where there are likely to be major impacts on agriculture, information collected from a desk exercise and discussions with the relevant organisations may need to be supplemented by Agricultural Land Classification survey work. Also, soil sampling and interviews with farmers may be needed.

Forestry: a description of plantation types and sizes, yield classes and land ownership and tenure. Where there are likely to be major impacts on forestry, discussions may need to be held with the main forestry operators, as well as the Forestry Commission.

Minerals and Waste Treatment and Disposal: a description of the current status of activities in the area, i.e. active sites and their anticipated life and after-use, outstanding permissions and newly granted permissions. Such information can normally be obtained from the mineral planning and waste regulation authorities.

Recreation: a description of current facilities for formal and informal recreation on and surrounding the site, including types of user (eg clubs or general public), levels of use, seasonal and daily variations in use. In the case of informal recreation, consideration may need to be given to sites with de facto access as well as designated areas of open space. Public rights-of-way will also need to be addressed fully where they are likely to be affected. Much of this information should be available from the local authority although a survey of clubs may be necessary to assess the use of private facilities. The use of public rights-of-way can usually be assessed from site visits combined with discussions with a local representative of the Parish Council.

Prediction of Impacts

18. The range of impacts which different types of development might have on each land use is too diverse to cover here, but in general methods for predicting the impacts of development on agriculture, forestry, and sites reserved for mineral extraction or waste disposal, are based on the application of knowledge from previous research and practical experience. They are usually qualitative in nature. There are, however, cases where impacts may be assessed using cost-benefit analysis, particularly in relation to agricultural development and forestry. Studies of the impact of development on recreational sites and resources can draw on a substantial range of research into visitor attitudes and preferences but any judgement about the effects which a particular development may have on existing or potential recreational resources is likely to be largely subjective.

Mitigation of Impacts

19. Where conflicts of interest arise between proposals for new development and the need to protect mineral resources or waste disposal facilities, there may be few opportunities for introducing mitigating measures. However, it is sometimes possible to bring forward the resource development programme to the mutual benefit of both types of development. For example, sand and gravel, brick clay and opencast coal reserves can sometimes be extracted in advance of, or as part of, the new development thus avoiding the need to sterilise land. In the case of agriculture, forestry and recreation, there are often ways in which the potential negative impacts of development can be mitigated, including the exchange of land, planting of new woodlands, and provision of alternative recreational facilities.

Selected Sources of Further Information

- Circular 18/87 Development involving Agricultural Land (1987) (Scotland) (Amended by circular 29/88)
- Draft National Planning Policy Guideline - Sport and Physical Recreation - Scottish Office (1995)
- Environmental Assessment (Afforestation) Regulations 1988 (SI 1207)
- Environmental Assessment (Scotland) Regulations 1988, part v
- Environmental Assessment - the Treatment of Landscape and Countryside Recreational Issues - the Countryside Commission
- Guidelines for Landscape and Visual Impact Assessment - the Landscape Institute and the Institute of Environmental Assessment (1995)
- Land Drainage Improvement Works (Assessment of Environmental Effects) Regulations 1988 (as amended)
- Minerals Planning Guidance Notes
- National Planning Guideline - Agricultural Land - Scottish Office (1987)
- Planning Policy Guidance Note 7 - the Countryside and the Rural Economy - Department of the Environment / Welsh Office (1992)
- Planning Policy Guidance Note 17 - Sport and Recreation - Department of the Environment/Welsh Office (1991)
- Revised Guidelines and Criteria for Grading the Quality of Agricultural Land in England and Wales - MAFF
- Waste Management Paper No 27, Landfill Gas - HMSO (1991)

FLORA AND FAUNA (ECOLOGY)

1. The assessment of ecological impacts[1] should cover both habitats and species of flora and fauna (especially protected species) and may need to include both terrestrial and aquatic ecosystems depending upon the nature of the development. It should include both the proposed site and its surroundings.

2. EAs of planning projects will be concerned primarily with terrestrial and freshwater ecology since developments affecting the marine environment do not generally fall under the control of Town and Country Planning legislation. However, terrestrial developments may affect the marine environment for example, where pipelines are built to discharge effluent to tidal waters. There may also be an effect on the relationship between land and sea in terms of barrages, reclamation, marinas and so on.

POTENTIAL IMPACTS

3. Major developments may be sited across different habitats of varying importance for nature conservation, while small developments may be proposed within a single area of high nature conservation importance. The aim should be that the least sensitive areas within the overall site are identified for development, unavoidable impacts minimised, and opportunities for enhancing the nature conservation interest of the site maximised.

4. Development may have both direct and indirect impacts on the natural environment. The most obvious direct effect is the physical removal of soils and vegetation, and the obliteration or substantial modification of existing habitats. This can be caused by the development and its access routes. Roads may affect the movement of wildlife if they cut across habitats, especially if traffic is heavy. If populations of scarce species are separated, their viability and thus survival may be reduced. Habitats may also be threatened by construction routes and working areas, or by the laying of services or pipelines. Potential indirect impacts are discussed below.

[1] Throughout the appendix, references to ecological impacts refer to both flora and fauna unless otherwise indicated.

Pollution

5. It can be very complex to trace the pathways by which pollutants affect individual plants and animals. Their effect is often cumulative and can be influenced by other environmental factors such as temperature and sunlight.

6. **Soil Pollution:** Pollution of soils can be caused by substances deposited on or in the land, by polluted precipitation, and by polluted groundwater. As in the case of air pollution, the misplacing of relatively harmless materials can have an adverse effect on local flora. For example, the deposit of nutrient-rich materials, such as sewage sludge, on nutrient-poor plant communities can irrevocably change species composition. Soil conditions can also greatly alter the effective toxicity of pollutants. Soil pollution is discussed in Appendix 6.

7. **Water Pollution:** Changes in water pH, such as that brought about by introducing water from one river system to another, can lead to adverse changes in aquatic species composition. Also, the accumulation of nutrients in aquatic sediments can cause ecological changes which are difficult to reverse. Water pollution is discussed in Appendix 7

8. **Air Pollution:** Three types of emissions may affect the natural environment: chemicals which directly or indirectly cause damage; apparently non-damaging materials which can cause chemical changes (such as alkaline dust from cement factories); and other particulates such as dust thrown up along haulage routes which smothers adjacent plants. Air pollution is discussed in Appendix 8.

Micro-climate

9. Where development is on a sufficiently large scale, or significant heat, light and radiation emissions are involved, the ambient or background conditions may be altered. Urban and industrial areas, for example, tend to retain heat and remain at higher temperatures during the winter than undeveloped rural areas. These micro-climatic changes may be sufficiently great to alter the performance of some species of plants and animals - although the primary influence is likely to be the manmade nature of the urban environment itself.

10. In the case of water, the release of heat in cooling water can cause significant changes in the receiving waterbody, especially where this is an enclosed system, such as a reservoir or lake.

Groundwater

11. In addition to potential pollution, development can have a profound effect on the groundwater regime as discussed in Appendix 7. This in turn may adversely affect any habitats dependent upon the watertable.

River Regimes

12. Increases or reductions in natural rates of flow are one of the primary ways in which aquatic ecosystems may be affected by development. Flash flooding may be caused by greater run-off associated with large areas of hard surfacing. Reduced flows, leading to siltation, may be directly related to increased water demand, or use of by-pass channels. In addition, changes brought about by flood alleviation schemes may affect surrounding habitats.

Public Pressure and Disturbance

13. New developments, especially those associated with recreation and residential use, may place surrounding or other nearby habitats under increasing public pressure. This can have a number of adverse effects on the natural environment including the disturbance of animals; the physical destruction of ground flora by horse and bike riding; and the increased risk of accidents, such as fire, which may lead to major habitat destruction.

Changing Relationship between Habitats

14. New developments can disrupt the established relationship between different habitats. For example, important habitats may be exposed to greater disturbance by the removal of surrounding 'buffer land', or routes linking sleeping or roosting areas to feeding grounds may be physically interrupted.

15. Fragmentation of a single large habitat by development may threaten the nature conservation value of remaining areas and, at the very least, may make the remaining fragments difficult to manage appropriately. For example, the traditional methods of chalk downland and heathland management, grazing or burning, are difficult to practise on a series of fragmented pieces of land separated by development.

16. Reduction or fragmentation of habitat size may reduce the population of key plant species, which in turn, may affect the abundance of the insects and butterflies they support. These may require a minimum area to sustain a viable population and may in turn affect other species, for example predatory birds.

Loss of Habitats at a Distance

17. In the case of some developments, habitats may be destroyed on a site or sites indirectly associated with the development. Most commonly this occurs in relation to the winning and disposal of materials, for example, the extension of quarries to provide building materials or landfill sites to accommodate wastes arising from the development. Projects for the winning or disposal of materials may require EA in their own right.

ASSESSMENT OF IMPACTS ON ECOLOGY

18. The effect of a development on the natural environment can be particularly complex and sometimes the range of indirect impacts will be much greater than the more obvious direct ones. It is important that a methodical and structured approach is adopted during the EA so that all the potential impacts are covered especially if rare or endangered species or habitats may be affected.

19. **Scoping:** The purpose of scoping in this context is:

    - to define the likely range and extent of impacts which the proposed development will have on the ecology, both during the construction and at the end, in the short and long term, and from this to establish the geographical areas for which ecological data should be collected;

    - to establish what information already exists on the ecology of the area likely to be affected whether directly or indirectly, and to supplement this information, as necessary, by initial site surveys;

    - based on appraisal of the above, to identify the key issues which should be addressed; and,

    - to identify any further survey work (especially surveys of fauna which can be very season-specific) which should be undertaken to complete the baseline surveys and allow an adequate assessment of impacts.

20. A habitat survey, which can also give a very general indication of the fauna present, will normally be sufficient for the scoping exercise. It should have enough detail to permit the identification of areas which are likely to be of high nature conservation value or particularly vulnerable to certain types of impact. However, care should be taken to ensure the survey covers fauna and flora present in all seasons.

21. Even some areas devoid of vegetation may be important habitats, especially mudflats and inland water bodies which may be of particular ornithological interest. Where information is needed urgently and either time or season precludes new survey work, an initial indication of the conservation interest of a site might be obtained from local specialists.

22. **Baseline Surveys:** The scoping exercise should identify the extent and nature of any further survey work that may be needed, but it may not always be possible to provide a complete picture of the existing ecological baseline.

23. **Flora:** Areas identified during scoping as being vulnerable to potential impacts should receive more detailed survey. This should identify species from all plant groups which form a significant part of the vegetation, not just higher plants.

24. **Fauna:** Some understanding of the probable value of a site for fauna can usually be gained from information collected during the vegetation survey. A number of publications are available which will assist in the identification of habitat types and features which are likely to be of value. However, where a full site assessment is required a more detailed survey will be necessary. This could involve the use of survey methodologies such as the British Trust for Ornithology's Common Bird Census technique for breeding birds.

25. The timing of surveys is a critical factor. For example, a different list of birds may be recorded breeding on a site in summer to those which over winter there; some species of invertebrates, such as butterflies, are on the wing for only short periods. Their activity is also highly weather dependent. This need for careful timing underlines the importance of identifying survey requirements at an early stage in the planning of a development.

26. Population levels of some species are subject to natural fluctuations which occur over many years. Baseline surveys conducted over a short period may not identify such long-term trends and, wherever possible, reference should be made to previous records.

Site Evaluation

27. The purpose of the evaluation stage is to assess the importance of the habitats and species likely to be affected by the development in a national, regional and local context.

28. Sites of national and international importance will almost certainly have some form of designation, though some sites have yet formally to be designated. The national network of Sites of Special Scientific Interest encompasses sites of international, national and regional importance. International designations include Ramsar sites (important wetlands) and Special Protection Areas under the EC Birds Directive, to which will be added Special Areas of Conservation under the Habitats Directive. In some areas, sites of local significance have been systematically evaluated. The EA should concentrate on evaluating those areas which have not been accorded any status by statutory bodies and comparing them with those which have.

29. A number of systems have been developed for the evaluation of sites. The more common attributes considered in such evaluations include size, species richness and diversity, rarity, typicality and naturalness (which may also be expressed as 'ancientness') or recreatability. As far as possible, evaluations should be objective.

30. Criteria such as size and rarity will need to be set in the context of surrounding areas to have any meaning, for example whether a species is locally, regionally or nationally rare. This will usually require reference to local flora and survey data and may be aided by discussion with relevant organisations. In the case of rarer species, reference should be made to specialist information.

31. **'Ancientness':** The term 'ancientness' has been particularly applied to woodlands. Often sites which have been stable over long periods have developed valuable communities which cannot usually be recreated. For woodlands, in particular, ancient sites are most commonly identified by their presence on old maps. The first editions of the Ordnance Survey six inch to one mile maps were published between the 1840s and the 1890s and cover the whole country. Maps from the late 1700a and early 1800s are also available for some areas.

32. This map evidence may be supplemented by site survey and the use of indicator species, that is those with precise requirements which restrict their distribution to distinctive habitats. The requirement is that they are common in the environment they indicate and rare elsewhere.

Prediction of Impacts

33. Having established the baseline conditions, the next step is to assess the likely impacts of the proposed development on this wildlife resource. Where habitats would be destroyed by the development, the assessment of impact is relatively straightforward but the anticipation of indirect impacts often has to be based, of necessity, on predictions rather than statements of fact.

34. Predictions may be based on past experience and be largely descriptive or they may be developed from laboratory experimentation, field trials and computer simulation. The assessment should finish with a statement of the significance of the identified impacts, requiring interpretation of findings and valuing the conclusions. This process is necessarily subjective and should therefore be undertaken by an experienced ecologist.

Determining the Significance of Impacts

35. When placing a value on the predicted impacts the ES will have to judge the significance of the impacts; for example, would they completely destroy a habitat, modify a habitat or marginally impinge on a habitat. It will also have to state whether the impacts are of national, regional or local significance depending on the status of the wildlife affected. This will draw directly on the earlier evaluation of wildlife importance. From this it will be possible to produce simple matrices indicating the significance of impacts on sites or species of national, regional and local status.

36. The assessment should also differentiate between short and long term impacts. Where they are short term the assessment will need to consider the ability of the communities to recover as well as the magnitude of the initial impact. The timing of an impact can also be critical to its magnitude. For example, disturbance could have a major impact on birds during their breeding season but may be of much lower significance at other times of the year.

Mitigation of Impacts

37. If the process of EA starts early enough in planning the development, it should be possible to identify mitigation measures to reduce or compensate for the identified impacts. In terms of ecology, there is a wide range of mitigation measures which can be adopted to reduce the impact of individual developments. As for landscape, these measures can most usefully be subdivided under the headings of avoidance, reduction and compensation or remedy.

38. **Avoidance** is concerned with avoiding damage, such as locating the main development and its working areas and access routes away from areas of high ecological interest, fencing off sensitive areas during the construction period, or timing works to avoid sensitive periods. Mitigation measures should also address issues relating to the long-term management of habitats, such as ensuring that habitats within the development site continue to receive appropriate management.

39. **Reduction** concerns the scope for decreasing impacts through, among other things, modifications or additions to the design of the development, such as the creation of reed bed silt traps to prevent polluted water running directly into ecologically important watercourses. The preservation of "wildlife corridors" between habitats which would be separated by a proposed development may reduce the possible effects on some fauna.

40. **Remedies or Compensation** need to be considered when impacts cannot be avoided, and usually take the form of replacing, in some form, that which will be lost. Thus they may be concerned with the relocation of important grassland or heathland habitats from the development site to another area identified as suitable (using techniques such as soil or turf transfer). They can also involve the creation of new habitats to replicate those that have been lost.

41. The ES should not over-stress the possible benefits of such remedies. Techniques for relocating habitats are at an early stage and they are most unlikely to be as valuable as they were on their original site. Many habitats such as ancient woodlands are 'non-recreatable' and new ones cannot begin to match the value of the habitats lost. Even when recreating non-ancient habitats, it may take many years for the new habitat to achieve the desired maturity. Care must also be taken to ensure that the mitigation measures themselves do not carry adverse impacts.

Selected Sources of Further Information

- British Trust for Ornithology Common Bird Census (1983)
- Department of the Environment - PPG 9 - Nature Conservation, (1994)
- Guidelines for Baseline Ecological Assessment, Institute of Environmental Assessment (1995)
- Nature Conservancy Council Guidelines for the Selection of Biological SSSIs (1989)
- Nature Conservancy Council Handbook for Phase 1 habitat survey; a technique for environmental audit (1990)

Further Information may be available from

- **English Nature, Countryside Council for Wales (CCW), Scottish Natural Heritage** hold information on:

  Sites of Special Scientific Interest (SSSIs)

  Special Protection Areas

  Special Areas of Conservation

  Ramsar Sites

  National Nature Reserves

  Ancient Woodlands

- **Local Authorities** may hold information on

  Local Nature Reserves

  Information on sites of known nature conservation value

- **Other national and local bodies** (eg RSPB, local nature conservation trusts) may hold information about sites of known nature conservation value

Appendix

6

SOIL, GEOLOGY AND HYDROGEOLOGY

1. In an EA it is desirable that the term 'soil' should be used in its engineering sense to include not only top and subsoil but also underlying superficial deposits. Where relevant, solid geology and hydrogeology should also be taken into account. The analysis of these subjects should extend, where appropriate, to geomorphological features and processes such as erosion.

2. Soil and geology play an important part in determining the environmental character of an area. The nature and alignment of rocks have a major influence on the landform. Rocks and drift deposits provide the parent material from which soil is created and they influence the rate at which soil is formed. Soil chemistry and structure strongly influence the type of vegetation which occurs naturally in an area. The soil also has a considerable part to play in the attenuation of diffuse pollutants and has a considerable influence on the types of agricultural, horticultural and forestry practices an area can support.

3. Many types of development will have direct impacts on soil. Many types of development may cause geological impacts but these are especially associated with major civil engineering projects, mineral extraction and disposal of wastes to landfill.

POTENTIAL IMPACTS

Soil

4. Most soils have taken thousands of years to develop the physical and chemical characteristics which they have today. Almost all British soils have been managed or affected by man's activities, principally for agricultural purposes. Soil is not an unlimited resource and development can affect soils in a number of ways; loss or destruction, physical or chemical damage, or by damage to soil biology.

5. **Loss/Destruction:** The destruction of natural soils is an inevitable consequence of many development activities although the extent of loss may be reduced by prior soil stripping, careful handling and storage and subsequent replacement, as in the case of mineral extraction, or reuse elsewhere, for example in the restoration of derelict land.

6. **Physical Damage:** In their natural state most soils have a well developed horizontal layering. The physical characteristics (texture, structure and porosity) of these layers depend on weathering processes, the activity of soil invertebrates and plant roots and the activities of man. They determine the soil's ability to support the growth of crops and other vegetation as well as absorb and release water. The movement of air and water within the soil is very important to plant growth, while the movement of water through soils is important to the regime of many streams and rivers, in the recharge of groundwater.

7. Construction can have a number of adverse impacts on soil. The use of heavy machinery on site, particularly in wet weather, can cause severe soil compaction. This can occur both to soils being moved and those being traversed by machinery for other purposes. Soil compaction can greatly restrict root growth and adversely affect the drainage characteristics of the soil which in turn can reduce plant growth, result in increased surface runoff and thereby increase the risk of erosion and the increased transfer of pollutants to surface waters. Deterioration in the physical quality of soil can also occur through mixing contrasting soil materials or layers (eg topsoil with subsoil), through contamination by other materials (eg rock or wastes) and by careless reinstatement.

Chemical Damage and Effects Created by Contaminated Land

8. Many construction activities have the potential to contaminate soils on and adjacent to the site, either by accidental spillage of materials used in the development or by the mixing of soils with construction materials. In other situations land already contaminated by wastes and residues, and the presence of toxic or hazardous materials, some of which may be of natural origin, may pose threats to human health or impose other constraints on new development.

9. Soil pollution can occur from materials deposited directly onto or into the soil from the deposition of airborne pollutants or by material carried in groundwater.

10. **Inorganic Compounds:** Elevated levels of heavy metals such as lead, cadmium, mercury and copper are one of the main areas of concern. Metals occur at low concentrations in most soils (and agricultural fertilisers) and can occur naturally at high concentrations through weathering of metalliferous minerals. However, high concentrations are in the main the result of activities such as the direct disposal to land of wastes from mineral workings, industrial processes or the water industry (eg sewage sludge) or the deposition of particulates from the atmosphere. High concentrations can be toxic to plants, soil, fauna and humans.

11. A second group of inorganic compounds of concern are the salts. Soil salinity is only naturally high in coastal and estuarine marshes but can result in adverse impacts on soils, land use and natural habitats if such land is drained without adequate ameliorative treatment or such materials are relocated to a different site, as for use in restoration.

12. As well as such natural forms of salinity, salts are produced as a result of some industrial processes and can be found within industrial landfill. Some salts are known to be aggressive to building materials and can lead to structural failure. Where levels of salt in soil are high enough to cause concern then the building materials used must conform to Building Research Establishment guidelines, for example in BRE Digest 363 'Sulphate and acid resistance of concrete in the ground'.

13. **Organic Wastes:** Many of these are entirely of vegetable and animal origin and will not cause significant damage to soils, though mobile components such as nitrate can cause pollution of surface and groundwater. Other organic wastes may include substances which can build-up in the soil affecting long-term fertility or resulting in delayed pollution of water resources.

14. **Landfill Gases:** Gases, such as methane, may be produced by the breakdown of organic materials, such as food waste, paper and timber, in anaerobic conditions. These situations are frequently found on landfill sites. The resultant gas can inhibit plant growth if it is allowed to enter the soil layers and can present an explosive hazard if allowed to build up in concentrations in an enclosed space.

15. Waste Regulation Authorities have a duty to prevent waste facilities causing pollution of the environment or harm to human health. To do this they impose conditions on licences and monitor sites while they are operational. The effects of such conditions on the methane produced by landfill sites should be taken into account. See Waste Management Paper No 27, Landfill Gas, published by HMSO which offers information about development on or around landfill sites.

16. **Radionuclides:** Radioactive wastes are produced by the nuclear industry. Lower levels of radiation are used in medical and research work. Where these materials are present in significant quantities they can be extremely toxic. The disposal of such materials is very strictly controlled and, in consequence, any process which produces radioactive waste will need to be subject to the closest scrutiny.

Geology

17. Potential impacts on geology are wide-ranging and in the case of certain types of development can include the triggering of ground instability such as subsidence or landslides or the alteration of groundwater levels and flow. Since the development may trigger such effects outside of the limits of the development site, it is important to examine the geology and geomorphology outside of the site boundaries.

18. In addition to these wide-ranging effects, physical works may have direct impacts on geological features which are, in themselves, of scientific interest and importance. English Nature, Scottish Natural Heritage and the Countryside Council for Wales are responsible for identifying and protecting geological Sites

of Special Scientific Interest (SSSIs).

19. Approximately one third of geological SSSIs are man-made, many as a result of quarrying activity. However, quarrying can be damaging where features of earth science interest are threatened, for example where quarrying would damage important landforms or features such as underground caves.

20. Many geological SSSIs, including sites of international importance, are coastal cliffs; whose value relies on the exposures being kept fresh by continued erosion. Where coastal recession creates a problem because of proximity to buildings, there is often considerable pressure to find engineered solutions which themselves can obliterate the geological interest of a site. Even small scale works can inhibit the action of the sea leaving the cliffs to become stabilised and overgrown. Once the underlying strata are no longer accessible the site is of little value for teaching or research.

21. Other types of impact which may destroy or reduce the scientific value of geological SSSIs are excavation, loss or burial of mineral samples, afforestation and canalisation.

ASSESSMENT OF EFFECTS ON SOIL AND GEOLOGY

Scoping

22. As a wide range of issues may be relevant under the heading of soil and geology it is important to clarify at the scoping stage exactly which topics are to be covered and how they relate to other parts of the assessment. Impacts on soil and geology may be covered in separate chapters of the ES or as sub-sections of other chapters. For example, where the geological conditions are a primary reason for designation of an area as an SSSI, this may be covered under a chapter dealing with Ecology and Scientific Interest.

Baseline Studies

23. It is necessary to review the issues concerned with soil, geology and water at an early stage so that critical data may be gathered on the ground conditions and hydrogeology of the site. Where aquatic environments are affected information on current flows, sediment transport and related topics should be obtained as and when relevant.

24. **Geotechnical Studies:** Site investigation will be required before the design of the project is carried out. Where this reveals potential ground problems geotechnical assessment will be required as part of the engineering design.

25. **Contaminated Land:** Where soil contamination is suspected (whether natural or relating to past industrial workings, waste tips and landfill sites) a site

investigation should be undertaken to establish the impact of the development.

26. **Site Stability:** There may be problems of site instability such as natural erosion, slope instability, variable ground conditions and subsidence into cavities, or problems may be associated with previous human activities such as mining or landfill operations. On landfill sites settlement can continue for a long period after tipping has finished, as the material is compressed and as decay of the tipped material occurs. Such sites can also present hazards from landfill gases. As a result landfill sites are generally unsuitable for 'hard' forms of developments (eg buildings and structures) mainly because of the risk of gas rather than subsidence.

27. **Natural Gases:** Gases such as methane, carbon dioxide, oxygen deficient air and radon, may be emitted naturally from the ground in some areas. There is a need to assess the potential for these to affect development in such areas, and to take appropriate preventative measures.

28. **Soil:** The survey, analysis and classification of soil is a specialised area of science. Some background data are available from former governmental organisations but this may not be accurate at field level. For a full analysis on a field by field basis, a detailed soil survey would be required. Such a survey can be useful in assessing other impacts such as on agricultural land quality and groundwater.

Prediction of Impacts

29. **Soil:** Impacts relating to soil are most likely to result from contamination and loss and destruction.

30. **Chemical Impacts:** Rates of retention and degradation in soil of potential pollutants will have to be assessed where it is intended that wastes are to be spread on the land surface. Where wastes contain plant nutrients, it will be necessary to establish the extent to which these are taken up by plants or left to build up in the soil with the risk of leaching to the water environment. For land already contaminated and affected by a proposed development, the analysis of historic plans, records, maps and survey data may provide limited information about the way a site has been used and suggest the nature and type of chemicals likely to be present. Data on old waste disposal sites may be available from the waste regulation authority. However, in the absence of comprehensive surveys, it will usually only be feasible to provide a qualitative order of risk. Estimating the quantities of contaminants and waste, and the extent to which leachates may have travelled into the surrounding soil and rock requires specialist assessment.

31. **Loss and Physical Damage:** The total loss and destruction of agricultural soil has a self-evident impact but where soils are excavated and stored for reuse the level of damage and deterioration in soil quality will depend upon the types of earthmoving machinery employed, methods of handling, weather conditions, and methods and length of storage. A plan for the stripping, storage and

replacement of the soil should be developed and carried out in order to minimise soil damage as a result of development. Assessment of effects on soils requires a good baseline survey of soil types and knowledge of soils' response to different conditions.

32. **Geology:** Impacts relating to geology may be divided into two categories.

33. **Potential Hazards and Risk:** Proposed development may be subject to a number of geological and related hazards. These may include unstable slopes, underground cavities, emissions of gases, flooding and erosion of land.

34. Relevant factors should be taken into account in any preliminary feasibility study on proposed development and, where appropriate, should be investigated in detail by experts before development proceeds. If sufficient data are available mathematical models may provide a powerful predictive tool, particularly in acquatic environments. Successful preventative and precautionary works can usually be designed although these may sometimes have environmental disbenefits.

35. Those preparing an EA should consider which, if any, of the above factors need to be taken into account in general terms. For significant hazards it may be necessary to establish the risk to development and the surrounding environment in order to show that these matters have been properly considered. Information on risk assessment included in any ES should make clear the methods used and the observational data and models on which they are based.

36. Geological hazards within a specific site may lead to environmental problems outside its confines if the ground is disturbed. Similarly, the site may be vulnerable to hazards originating outside its boundaries. It is often necessary, therefore, to examine the geological characteristics of the environs of the site in addition to those of the site itself.

37. **Environmental Geology and Features of Scientific Interest:** Both direct and indirect effects may be caused to geological processes through new development. The assessment and prediction of these types of impact depends upon a review of case histories for previous developments of a similar nature, and the application of existing scientific principles to the particular details of the proposal and the site's geology.

Mitigation of Impacts

38. **Active Geological Processes:** Where active geological processes are taking place or may be triggered, careful attention to the siting and design of new development is the most effective way of anticipating future problems and minimising the initial impact. In circumstances where some disturbance of existing processes is inevitable, appropriate engineering techniques can be used to ameliorate or mitigate the effects, including use of drainage and stabilisation works, or

'bioengineering' using the roots of fast-growing trees and shrubs or reed mats.

39. **Contaminated Land:** Remedial strategies for dealing with contaminated land are likely to be site-specific and therefore each site will need to be considered on its own merits. Factors to be taken into consideration include the nature and concentration of the contaminants present, the hazards and risks they pose to various receptors, the current or intended use of the site, the hydrogeology and the availability and suitability of particular remedial treatments.

40. **Soil:** Methods for mitigating the impact on a soil's biological or physical state will depend on the proposed development. Physical barriers might need to be installed between some developments and adjacent soils. The impacts of proposals which involve soil stripping, storage and replacement can be mitigated by using certain earthmoving techniques and equipment, by vegetating stored soils and by carrying out ameliorative operations during and after soil reinstatement. Laying of geotextile matting can protect vulnerable soils from damage along temporary vehicular access routes. Displaced soils can be beneficially used elsewhere, as in reclamation of derelict land. Where the proposed development affects water tables the impact on nearby wetland soils can be mitigated by artificially maintaining water levels.

Selected Sources of Further Information

- British Standards Institute, BS DD175:1988 - Code of Practice for identification and investigation of contaminated land.
- Contaminated Land Research Report No 3 - Documentary Research on Industrial Sites - DOE Publications
- DOE Circular 30/92 - Development and Flood Risk (1992) - HMSO
- Land Classification Maps
- Minerals Planning Guidance Note 12 - Treatment of Disused Mine Openings and Availability of Information on Mined Ground (1994) - HMSO
- Policy Planning Guidance Note 14 - Development on Unstable Land (1990) - HMSO
- Policy Planning Guidance Note 23 - Planning and Pollution Control (1994) - HMSO

Further Information may be available from

- British Geological Survey

WATER

1. Any major development has the potential to affect the water environment, both directly on site and indirectly in the wider catchment (including potentially the estuarine and marine environment).

POTENTIAL IMPACTS

2. Impacts can relate to both **hydrological matters** and **water quality**. Impacts can also affect utilisation of the water environment, eg fisheries, recreation and navigation, but these are not addressed in this appendix.

Hydrological Impacts

3. Every catchment has its own hydrological characteristics which determine the balance of water flows between the different elements of the cycle including:

   - infiltration through soils to recharge groundwater
   - lateral flow through soils
   - surface flows as run-off to streams and drainage channels.

   The absorption of water by soil and vegetation, and its gradual release to adjacent drains and streams, helps to even out stream and river flow compared with the variability of rainfall incidents. The impact of a particular development on the hydrological cycle can be divided into effects on **surface water** and on **groundwater**.

4. **Surface Water Run-off:** A major effect of development can be to alter the land-surface characteristics and so affect the natural balance between surface and groundwater regimes. New developments often create large areas of impervious or semi-pervious surfaces which, combined with the provision of storm water drains, can increase peak flows in the watercourses while reducing the infiltration of water to groundwater and lateral flow. This can have a number of indirect effects including:

- increasing the occurrence and risk of flooding downstream;
- causing erosion on-site and downstream;
- reducing the recharge of aquifers.

5. Conversely, reduced flows in rivers and streams leading to siltation of channels may be directly related to increased water abstraction direct from the river or, as noted below, where abstraction from the underlying aquifer results in reduced spring flows.

6. Developments necessitating some form of flood protection can also alter river flows with consequent impacts on river flora and fauna. For example, the reduction in flood storage capacity may increase the flood risk either upstream or downstream of the area where protection works are undertaken, channel widening may lead to reduced rates of flow resulting in silt deposits, while channel straightening will increase river gradients leading to increased scouring.

7. Development in a flood plain below a reservoir should take into account two considerations. Firstly, the reservoir may be decommissioned, in which event flood frequency characteristics may change. Advice should be sought on the likelihood of this and if so, whether more severe and frequent flooding would result. Second, development downstream of a reservoir may change the safety hazard rating for that reservoir and require more expensive dam improvement works.

8. **Groundwater:** Where recharge of groundwater is reduced, a fall in the water table may follow with significant implications for water table-dependent habitats on and surrounding the site. This can be aggravated by extensive trenching, for drains and pipes, which may act effectively as land drains.

9. Water supply for domestic purposes, irrigation and industrial processes is of fundamental concern to groundwater sources. Increased supply, depending on the type and nature of the aquifer, can have significant impacts on its quality and quantity both on site and over much larger areas. Where abstraction exceeds natural recharge, it may lead to a marked seasonal or even permanent fall in water table levels. Not only can this lead to a loss of habitats but it may also result in reduced river flows as the natural springs which feed the river system dry up.

10. Development may also affect groundwater movement. Landfill, major foundations and service trenches can act as a barrier to groundwater, leading to a rise in water table levels on the upstream side and a fall in water table levels on the downstream side. Examples of other construction activities which may arise in connection with a range of projects and their implications for the water environment are summarised below.

Examples of Construction Activities and Their Potential Effects on the Aquatic Environment

Dredging : can destroy bottom dwelling organisms, and affect mobile organisms. The site of dumped materials must also be considered.
Land reclamation : can radically alter the habitat of the area concerned. Site preparation including building of roads and levelling can release sediments such as sand and gravel which find their way into waterbodies disrupting the aquatic system.
Channelisation : can change the aquatic habitat through the widening, straightening and confinement of a natural watercourse within manmade banks and bed with consequent effects on wildlife.
Filling : can alter the habitat by reducing the volume of water and changing its physical, chemical and biological properties.
Shoreline modification : can lead to loss or change of a habitat, and also to changes in sediment movement affecting erosion or deposition further along the coast.
Clearing of vegetation : if vegetation is left in a waterbody it may be broken down by micro-organisms, leading to deoxygenation and release of nutrients, which may give rise to algal blooms. Species may be replaced or eliminated completely with no additions taking their place.
Ditching - can bring about sedimentation by releasing excavated material into the watercourse.
Impounding - can change aquatic habitat types by converting free-flowing rivers or streams, or estuaries, into areas of still water .
Run-off from the site when plant is operational may be of a kind to contaminate sections of nearby waterbodies.

Water Quality Impacts

11. Water pollution is a complex subject and it is only possible to touch here on some of the known and potential effects.

12. Two important considerations in the assessment of the impact of pollution on the water environment are:

    - first, the concentration of any given pollutant in a waterbody and the period of time during which it may be in contact with a sensitive species or community;

    - second, the likely effects these concentrations will have on aquatic life and on human beings and animals who consume or otherwise use the water.

13. Consideration should be given not only to the potential water quality implications of a project on purely biological or toxicological grounds, but also to effects on landscape and visual amenity, availability of water for abstraction to potable supply, recreation, aquatic ecology (including riverbanks and river dependent species) and the economic, nuisance and health impacts on human beings and animals.

14. **Sources of Water Pollution:** Pollution may enter the aquatic system from a number of sources which will vary greatly depending on the nature of the site and type of development. Some potential sources include:

- discharges from sewage works and industrial plants at identifiable point sources;
- intermittent discharges from such sources as storm flows and land run-off;
- continuous leaching from ground within which the waterbody is enclosed including pollutants in groundwater entering the system;
- deposition of materials from the air (for example acid rain), or spray drift during application of pesticides and related products;
- miscellaneous events such as accidental or deliberate spillage or dumping;
- releases from dead or decaying aquatic flora and fauna; and
- releases from construction activities.

15. **Types of Water Pollution:** Water pollution is the introduction by man of substances or energy into the aquatic environment which are likely to cause hazards to human health, harm to living resources and ecosystems, damage to structures or amenities, or interference with other legitimate uses of water. Water pollutants include heavy metals, organic wastes, inorganic wastes, suspended solids, reducing agents, toxic substances, heat and oil. But it could also include invasive or competitive species, such as farmed fish, escaping into the river. The main effects that pollutants have on the aquatic ecosystem include:

- reducing the concentration of dissolved oxygen;
- increasing the risk of contracting infection death or affecting reproductive potential;
- altering the habitat or interfering with food chains;
- decreasing the quality available for abstraction to potable supply; and,
- reducing the aesthetic quality of the habitat.

Although a pollutant may not be present in toxic concentration, there may a cumulative effect eg due to its build-up in an aquatic food chain.

16. Parameters which can be used to assess pollution levels include physical (such as odour, solids and oils), chemical (such as salinity, heavy metals and pesticides), microbiological (such as faecal coliforms and viruses) and hydrobiological (such as fish and aquatic plants).

17. **Effects on Water Quality:** The effects of pollution on the receiving water quality are highly dependent on the type and concentration of the pollutants (and on the nature of the waterbody receiving the pollution, e.g. existing quality, volume, mixing characteristics etc). Potential effects of particular pollutants include for example, excessive nitrogen and phosphorus which can lead to algal blooms with associated water treatment problems, and chlorides which cause a salty taste in the water.

18. **Effects on Water Resources:** Not only is pollution of concern with regard to receiving watercourses but also with regard to groundwater and aquifers. The regulatory agencies will wish to ensure that adequate safeguards have been employed with respect to all major development which has the potential to generate pollution of watercourses and aquifers.

ASSESSMENT OF THE EFFECTS ON WATER

19. **Scoping:** During scoping the available water resource and water quality data should be identified and additional monitoring requirements determined.

20. **Baseline Surveys:** This initially involves collecting information on the current condition of the water environment. Depending on the type of development, this may include catchment areas and characteristics, drainage patterns, channel details (including flow regimes), details of waterbodies etc. The assembling of existing information from sources such as the NRA in England and Wales and the River Purification Authorities in Scotland (whose consent is normally required for the discharge of trade or sewage effluent), and local authorities, should provide some of the required baseline information but any additional monitoring necessary, as identified in the scoping stage, should be completed for the baseline survey.

21. The assembling of information should focus primarily on anticipated surface and groundwater impacts and potential pollutants associated with the proposed development during the construction and the operational stages. The baseline survey should also relate the current conditions to projected trends and the effect that such changes could have on the potential impacts of the development.

22. **Prediction of Impacts:** The prediction of impacts following on from the scoping and baseline stages should focus on those identified as significant. These should be considered during all the phases of the development: construction, operation

and post-operation. Consideration of whether downstream effects need modelling requires a structured approach. First, it should be established that there may be a problem. Second, if a problem is likely, a simple fluvial model may suffice to provide an understanding of the sensitivity of a watercourse to changes in discharge, flow regime, sediment load etc. Third, and more complex, any consequential effects on flora and fauna should be identified both within the river channel and adjacent habitats.

23. In order to evaluate the impact of projected changes against the existing situation, professional skills will be required. The potential impact should be judged against appropriate criteria, standards or policies. These may include, for example, relevant policies within local planning documents or those promoted by the NRA in England and Wales or the River Purification Authorities in Scotland.

24. Standards for water quality have been laid down under EC legislation. The DoE and the NRA, and in Scotland the River Purification Authorities, have established enforceable environmental quality standards (EQS) for a wide variety of substances. The NRA also operates system of informal river quality objectives (RQOs) which are the basis for all water quality planning. Information about these can be obtained from the NRA.

25. **Mitigation of Impacts:** Mitigation measures can be utilised in the planning and construction of a given project so as to minimise undesirable effects on the aquatic environment. They could include for example:

- employment of appropriate design criteria and management procedures to ameliorate surface water and ground water impacts, including drainage systems and balancing ponds;

- modification to plant design to minimise or eliminate the presence of a particular substance from the waste stream;

- changes in design of waste effluent treatment plant or in method of waste treatment;

- changes in waste management practices such as discharge rates, land application rates of potential pollutants etc.

Selected Sources of Further Information

- Department of the Environment, Circular 30/92, Development and Flood Risk (1992)
- National Planning Policy Guideline 7 - Planning and Flooding, Scottish Office (1995)
- Planning Policy Guidance Note 23, Planning and Pollution Control, Department of the Environment (July 1994)
- Policy and Practice for the Protection of Groundwater, National Rivers Authority : Reading (1992)
- River Corridor Surveys - Methods and Procedures Conservation Technical Handbook No 1 - National Rivers Authority, Reading (1992)

Further Information may be available from

- Her Majesty's Industrial Pollution Inspectorate (Scotland)
- Her Majesty's Inspectorate of Pollution
- National Rivers Authority
- River Purification Authorities (Scotland)

Appendix

8

AIR AND CLIMATE

1. The assessment of air quality impacts can be one of the most complex elements of an EA due to the range of different pollutants that may be emitted, the combination of pollutants to form secondary pollutants, the effects of local climate and topography, and the variety of different scales at which the effects of air pollution may be experienced. Some pollutants may have very local, mainly health related impacts. Others may produce effects at a national or international scale. Those carrying out the EA should take account of non-planning controls over air pollution.

2. Sources of air pollution may be described as either stationary (eg industrial or domestic chimneys) or mobile (those emissions associated with transport activity). Stationary sources may, in turn, be classified as point sources, such as large chimneys, or area sources. The latter may include areas comprising a number of small point sources, or may be emission sources such as waste treatment tanks and opencast mineral workings. Mobile emission sources include vehicles' exhausts (including those from aircraft), and also the dust associated with the movement of minerals or other materials.

3. The complexity of the factors affecting air quality is reflected in the methods that are used for both the measurement and the prediction of air pollution. In some situations it may also be appropriate to model the existing situation eg emissions from existing traffic flows. Unless air quality measurements are carried out over a long period, modelled results can give a better representation of emission levels for comparison with predicted future levels, and air quality standards and guidelines.

TYPES OF AIR POLLUTION AND THEIR EFFECTS

4. There are many significant air pollutants from a variety of sources and with varied potential effects. They include asbestos, benzene, methane, cadmium, sulphur dioxide and suspended particulates, as well as unpleasant odours. Some are particularly toxic, and represent potential health hazards to human beings, though it should be noted that the impacts of air pollution on human health are highly variable according to the age and health of the population, the type of pollutants concerned, their concentration, and the period of exposure.

POTENTIAL IMPACTS

5. Although it is essential that the possible air quality impacts of development are assessed on a case by case basis, it is possible to make a number of generalisations regarding potential impacts.

6. Proposals which involve significant movements of earth, coal or other minerals are likely to generate problems of dust. Such schemes include opencast mineral workings, the reclamation of derelict land and the storage of minerals above ground. Other sources of dust may include processing industries such as cement manufacture and the construction phases of large projects such as airports.

7. Any activity which involves the combustion of fossil fuels is likely to result in the emission of pollutants including sulphur and nitrogen oxides, carbon monoxide and carbon dioxide. Such developments may include coal and oil fired power stations, industrial and commercial heating systems and industrial processes such as metallurgy or glass making.

8. Proposals which involve the refining, use or movement of chemicals may involve planned emissions of very specific types, requiring detailed investigations and understanding of the processes involved. Given the potential impact on air quality of a chemical spillage, risk assessment of such proposals should be carried out as a matter of course. The level of detail in the risk assessment should be related to the perceived hazards.

9. Many activities have significant transport implications, either during construction or use. Such proposals may result in a wide variety of emission types depending on the characteristics of the transport mode and individual vehicle type involved. Typical pollutants include benzene, nitrogen and sulphur oxides, lead, carbon monoxide, carbon dioxide and particulates.

AIR QUALITY STANDARDS AND GUIDELINES

10. Air quality standards and guidelines provide the means of assessing whether existing, or predicted, levels of air pollution exceed currently acceptable limits. There are two main sources for such standards and guidelines.

11. The 1989 Air Quality Standards Regulations (SI 317/1989) implement EC Directives setting air quality limit (mandatory) and guide (non-mandatory) values for sulphur dioxide and suspended particulates (Directive 80/779), a limit value for lead in air (Directive 82/884) and air quality standards for nitrogen dioxide (Directive 85/203). As the terms suggest, limit values describe concentrations of pollutants which must not be exceeded, while guide values are intended to serve as long term precautions for health and the environment. The Regulations require the Secretary of State to ensure that the levels of these pollutants are monitored and reduced below specified limit values.

12. The World Health Organisation has published non-mandatory air quality guidelines for Europe with the aim of 'protecting public health from adverse effects of air pollution and for eliminating, or reducing to a minimum those contaminants of air that are known or likely to be hazardous to human health and well-being'. The guidelines are based on analysis of the lowest concentration at which effects are observed in humans, animals and plants. A range of guideline figures has been produced, reflecting both the method of measurement and the exposure period. The guidelines cover, among other substances, carbon monoxide, nitrogen dioxide, sulphur dioxide, particulate matter, formaldehyde, lead, ozone and asbestos.

13. Other air quality guidelines may exist in particular areas of the country, particularly if local authorities have included pollution policies in development plans. The Department of the Environment has established an independent Expert Panel on Air Quality Standards to develop standards for the UK for the purposes of guiding air pollution control policy.

AIR QUALITY MONITORING, MEASUREMENT AND PREDICTION

14. Sulphur dioxide and smoke (particulates) are monitored at over 250 sites throughout the UK. There are also a number of urban and suburban stations monitoring ground level concentrations of nitrogen dioxide, and sites monitoring concentrations of airborne lead. In 1988 a national network monitoring ground level ozone was established by the Department of the Environment. In addition to these national networks, many local authorities also monitor air quality, sometimes focussing on emissions of particular local significance. There are a range of methods for measuring air pollution.

15. The most common means of forecasting future levels of air pollution is to undertake a computer modelling exercise. Details of the emission source characteristics, together with data describing local climate and topography, form inputs to a computer model which will predict ground level emission concentrations in the vicinity of a proposed development. The results can then be compared with air quality standards and guidelines to determine acceptability of the air pollution impact.

THE OZONE LAYER

16. Depletion of the ozone layer is a world-wide problem which requires global cooperation if it is to be tackled effectively. The Montreal Protocol on Substances that Deplete the Ozone Layer was set up in 1987 and introduced controls on the main depleting substances. These have since been tightened. Within the EC, production of CFC's, halons and carbon tetrachloride has already ceased and others are being phased out.

17. Developers should keep abreast of changes in regulations and requirements relating

to man-made chemicals and their use, and ensure that any potential effects arising from their proposed schemes are acknowledged and considered in the EA. Products should not be used if they contain gases that deplete the ozone layer, and all refrigeration and air conditioning equipment should be properly maintained, including leakage prevention and recovery of refrigerants.

CLIMATE CHANGE

18. Predictions of greenhouse gas emissions arising from a development will require consideration of factors such as the amount and form of energy used, impacts on transport patterns, and, in certain cases, such as landfill sites, prediction of methane emissions. In the case of power stations, both the efficiency of the generating process and the type of fuel used will be important in determining future carbon dioxide emissions. Where electricity will be generated from non-fossil sources, consideration should be given to the indirect reductions in emissions from the fossil fuel burning displaced. Use of emissions factors relating carbon dioxide production to fuel consumption are likely to be required in making predictions. Emission factors vary with fuel type. Carbon dioxide emissions per unit of electricity are expected to decrease over the next decade with changes in the fuel mix in the energy generating industry, but electricity will remain more carbon intensive than other energy sources.

19. Methods to limit greenhouse gas emissions may include use of energy efficient buildings, use of renewable energy or combined heat and power technology, direct control measures such as flaring or utilization of methane arising from landfills, and measures to reduce the amount of traffic attracted by the development. (The Government is committed under the UN Climate Change Convention to take measures aimed at returning emissions of greenhouse gases to 1990 levels by the year 2000.)

20. Information and guidance is often available which can help in assessing how the approach proposed for a development compares with best environmental practices. Information on how to maximise energy efficiency in buildings and industrial processes is available through the 'Best Practice' Programmes run by the DoE (Environmental and Energy Management Directorate 0171 276 6200).

ASSESSMENT OF THE EFFECTS ON AIR POLLUTION

21. **Scoping:** Scoping is a very important stage in the assessment of air pollution impacts, not least because of the large number of potential pollutants and their effects. The aim of this exercise is to identify those pollutants which are likely to be of concern given the general characteristics of the development and its proposed location. From the developer's point of view, the scoping process can help reduce the costs of undertaking the EA by defining which possible pollutants do not require monitoring and prediction. Conversely, the exercise may allow other

interested parties to ensure that issues of concern to them are made known to the developer. Scoping should identify the air pollution and meteorological data that already exist, and the areas where additional monitoring will be necessary.

22. **Baseline Surveys:** Collection of baseline air pollution data provides the basis against which the impact of the proposed development will be judged. Given the costs and complexity of undertaking monitoring and prediction of air quality, the baseline survey should closely reflect the findings of the scoping exercise and focus on the likely emissions of the proposed development. The baseline survey should comprise the assembly of existing and relevant air quality data (derived from national or local monitoring networks), the collation of local meteorological data, and the completion of any additional air or climatic monitoring that was identified by the scoping exercise.

23. It is essential that any monitoring which is carried out is appropriate to the pollutant in question. For instance, monitoring of sulphur dioxide in an urban area should reflect the fact that sulphur dioxide levels are at their highest during the winter when buildings are being heated. Calm weather conditions may result in temperature inversions leading to significantly inflated baseline readings for certain pollutants. Conversely, wet or windy weather may result in suppressed readings. Where relevant records exist, the baseline survey should include an analysis of air quality trends. This will give a much more accurate impression of conditions than if only one year is examined, and may indicate that air quality has consistently improved or deteriorated over a number of years. Such information is essential for the accurate interpretation of air pollution predictions.

24. **Prediction of Impacts:** Building on the findings of the scoping exercise, the prediction of future air pollution impacts should focus on those emissions that have been identified as potentially significant. The project should be broken down into its constituent phases (for instance site reclamation, construction, use, and decommissioning) and the air quality impacts of each stage assessed. The comprehensiveness of analysis will depend on the number and type of development phases.

25. Future levels of air pollution are usually calculated using a mathematical model of pollution dispersal. Inputs to this analysis include the characteristics of the proposed development, or phases of development (i.e. nature and volume of emissions, height and location of chimneys, vents etc), and the nature of the local topography and meteorology. The emission characteristics of the proposed development may be estimated in a number of ways, including the use of data derived from similar developments elsewhere. Such data is likely to include analysis of fuel type and fuel consumption of boilers, power plants and vehicles and the use of emission factors that have been calculated for particular industrial or transport activities. Where scoping and baseline stages have indicated that existing local sources of pollution exist, these should be included in the analysis.

26. **Mitigation of Impacts:** The prediction of likely air pollution impacts of a development (which take into account the existing air quality identified during the scoping survey) will determine whether it is probable that it will result in a breach of a relevant air quality standard or guideline. This analysis may well indicate that the development has no significant air pollution impacts. However, even where standards or guidelines are breached, mitigating measures (for instance the modification of an industrial process, or the use of more efficient plant) may be employed to bring the development within the prescribed limits.

27. The use of such mitigation measures emphasises the fact that environmental assessment is a process which, when properly employed, should result in a more efficient and less environmentally damaging development. In many cases, the mitigating measures proposed as a result of an environmental assessment will reduce costs for the developer, by encouraging the use of the cleanest available plant, and by making it less likely that further pollution reducing measures will need to be 'bolted on' to existing plant at a later stage.

Selected sources of Further Information

- Air Quality Standards Regulations 1989 ; SI 317
- Clean Air Act 1993
- Environmental and Energy Management Directorate, Best Practice Programme
- Environmental Protection Act 1990
- Policy Planning Guidance Note 23 - Planning and Pollution Control - Department of the Environment (July 1994)

LANDSCAPE

1. Landscape is a product of the interaction between a range of physical and biological characteristics and the cultural heritage. It encompasses not only the physical features of landform and surface pattern but also the way in which these features are perceived, and the values which are attached to scenery by people. This approach recognises that landscape is a fundamental component of the wider environment and is not just associated with a limited number of designated areas of particular scenic value.

POTENTIAL IMPACTS

2. An EA should consider two key types of landscape impact: direct effects on landscape resources, and public perception of landscape change.

Direct Effects on Landscape

3. Development of all kinds can have a direct effect on landscape resources by altering them or removing them completely. In considering such direct effects, an assessment should review:

   - the character and history of the existing landform and surface pattern of landscape affected, including the contribution of key landscape elements;

   - the nature and extent of the landscape changes likely to take place and options for mitigating changes;

   - the status of the landscape in terms of national, regional and local designations, including reference to management arrangements; and,

   - the significance of impacts in terms of value attached to the affected landscape (based on scenic quality, rarity, typicality etc).

Public Perception of Landscape Change

4. The following issues need to be considered:

   - the location of public vantage points overlooking the development site and the degree of visibility which exists at each location. Areas identified in this way are often referred to as lying within the 'zone of visual influence'.

   - visual characteristics of the proposal in relation to its surroundings, including scale, form, height, colour, materials etc;

   - the identification of those who will perceive the changes, including residents and visitors to the area;

   - the magnitude and significance of the perceived changes in the landscape quality, including degree of visual assimilation.

5. Organisations and groups of people with a particular interest in the landscape quality of a development site may include:

   - **government agencies,** such as the Countryside Commission, the Countryside Council for Wales, English Heritage and Scottish Natural Heritage, and local authorities, whose policies are expressed by designations such as Areas of Outstanding Natural Beauty, National Scenic Areas, Historic Landscapes and conservation areas, county regional landscapes of special significance etc.

   - **amenity groups and others with special interests** in valued landscapes. In considering the public response to landscape issues, it may be helpful to consult with statutory consultees, groups such as the National Trust and the National Trust for Scotland and other national environmental groups, and with local amenity groups. It may also be useful to take into account the work of artists and writers who have been inspired by the landscape in question since these are often important influences on the way landscapes are valued;

   - **parish and community councils and local residents** who will be most directly affected by the visual (and other) impacts of the scheme, because they can see it from their homes and other points in the locality. This group will be concerned both with personal amenity in terms of effects on their own homes and lives, and with community interest in local landscapes;

   - **visitors to the area** who may have a range of different perceptions, because they make use of the landscape for different purposes.

6. The landscape assessment should cover the direct effects, both long and short term, on the landscape and on the perceived value which people attach to the landscape. The effects of both the construction phase and the operation stage of

the development should be considered. Detailed consideration will also need to be given to indirect and off-site effects including, for example, traffic-generation. Secondary development pressures arising from the main proposal, such as the possible need for new housing or road improvements, should also be considered where necessary.

ASSESSMENT METHODOLOGY

7. In order to carry out an assessment of the impacts of a development on landscape and perceived landscape values, a combination of two methods can be used:

- **Landscape assessment** should provide a clear description of landscape character to give a picture of the existing situation;

- **Techniques for visual impact assessment** should define the 'zone of visual influence' of a development, assessing the visual intrusion to different user-groups and presenting illustrations of the nature of the impact; and the options for mitigating these impacts.

LANDSCAPE ASSESSMENT

8. National agencies and other organisations concerned with landscape and countryside protection have long sought to develop methods for classifying landscape types and attributing values to landscapes of differing qualities. Strategic assessments have been undertaken at regional, county and district level to assist in the formulation of structure plan, unitary development plan and local plan policies; and for specific objectives like the development of indicative strategies for forestry, or countryside management.

9. Where a landscape assessment has been prepared and adopted as the basis of a statutory or advisory plan, it may not be necessary for the promoter to carry out much additional work. But where a major development is proposed in an area which has not been surveyed in this manner, it will be appropriate to carry out a landscape assessment of the site and its surroundings. The purpose is to classify broad tracts of countryside into distinct landscape 'types' or 'units', as a basis for analysing the physical properties and quality of each area, the influences which this should have on the design of the project and any mitigating measures proposed.

10. Landscape character assessments invariably require a balance of objective and subjective techniques. Objective techniques usually involve measurement, arrangement and quantification of the various components which make up a landscape. Subjective approaches, on the other hand, rely on the judgements and responses of the surveyor. They are generally much more descriptive and seek to evoke the aesthetic characteristics of a landscape and the reactions of people to it.

11. In practice, the distinction between objective and subjective techniques is seldom clear cut. Even in surveying the elements which make up a landscape, or in defining key features and classifying landscape types, which many might consider to be objective matters, subjective judgements have to be made by the assessor.

12. Methods of assessment should incorporate both approaches distinguishing as far as possible between those parts which are largely objective, dealing with the nature of the landscape itself, and those which are subjective dealing with reactions to the landscape.

13. The stages that may be addressed as part of a landscape assessment include an inventory/description, classification and evaluation, and may include a combination of written description, maps, sketches and photographs. Useful information is available in the book "Guidelines for Landscape and Visual Impact Assessment (1995)" published jointly by the Landscape Institute and the Institute of Environmental Assessment.

Landscape Description

14. The description of the objective elements of the landscape can be divided into landform, landcover and landscape elements:

- **landform** covers all under lying structural and the physical factors which define and describe features of the landscape, such as topography and underlying geological controls; surface drainage systems; soils; particular evidence of current landform processes (erosion, deposition, unstable slopes etc);

- **landcover** considers the main vegetation and land use characteristics; and,

- noteworthy **landscape elements** which include key slopes and sky lines, buildings and structures, trees, hedges and other important small-scale vegetation features.

15. The interrelationship between these three provides the overall character of the landscape. This can be described in both a written and visual form. Maps, sketches and photographs may all contribute to the visual information along with descriptions which may also include the surveyor's subjective reactions to the landscape in terms of its aesthetic and tranquil qualities.

Landscape Classification

16. An important product of landscape assessment is to divide the area under consideration into sections of common character. These are often referred to as landscape units or types. This approach emphasises that landscapes are more than just a sum of component parts, by describing how different units relate to one another.

17. A landscape classification may already exist in some form for the area. It may have been carried out for example, by a county or regional planning authority in preparing their structure plan. Where it does exist, it may be used as the basis for landscape classification in the environmental statement.

18. The existing landscape character should also be described within the context of any likely change in the future, as the appearance of the landscape at a particular time is a result of the interaction of land use management upon the underlying physical and biological structure. This will enable the effects of the proposed development to be judged against a potentially changing landscape.

Landscape Evaluation

19. The evaluation of landscape qualities falls into two parts:

- an assessment of the way in which the landscape has been perceived over the years, and the way it is perceived today; and,

- preparation of a summary statement about why the landscape is important.

VISUAL IMPACT ASSESSMENT

20. Having examined and evaluated the landscape character of the area in which the proposal is situated, the 'zone of visual influence' of the proposal should then be determined. The visual impact is a function both of the area from which it can be seen, and the character of the surrounding landscape. This can best be established from a combination of desk study using O.S. maps and aerial photographs (if they are available) cross checked against the results of field survey. The limits of the 'visual envelope' or 'viewshed' may be defined as the area from which it is possible to see the proposed site, subject to intervening obstacles such as high walls, fences, hedges, buildings, trees and woodland.

21. This may be done manually by interpreting contours on an O.S. map or by using a digital terrain model computer programme to calculate the areas from which the development might be seen. The area which is covered in this way - the normal extent of the 'zone of visual influence' - will depend on the scale and nature of the development. This zone may be large if, for example, there are views across open water, or the proposed development is on high ground (for example the zone of visual influence for a particular windfarm development in Britain has been calculated to be approximately 10 miles), or itself involves large scale structures. The visual influence zone may be small if the site uses actual landscape features as screening or is situated in areas of subdued relief.

Evaluation of Visual Impact

22. The significance of the development's impact on the landscape needs to be judged

on the basis of the extent to which it adversely affects the 'zone of influence'. The evaluation should be based on a carefully selected number of representative viewpoints, each of which should be visited to judge to what extent the presence of the proposal would detract from, or enhance, the character of the landscape. In particularly sensitive locations, site visits may be necessary at different times of day or in differing weather conditions and at different times of the year (eg. to evaluate the changing effectiveness of broad leaved woodlands as "screening").

23. The choice of viewpoints should reflect the interaction of the proposed development and the most important aspects of the landscape. The locations should reflect both distant and close views, such as the view from public roads, public access areas etc within the zone of visual influence.

24. There are a number of methods of representation to simulate the appearance of proposed development and these can be a great help when inspecting the site. They include:

- **Sketches and scale drawings;**

- **Computer generated pen cross-sections and perspectives:** provide accurate dimensions and are useful in the design process but are less effective at representing the colour and texture of landscape or illustrating fine detail;

- **Three dimensional models:** can be useful in the early stages of design, but are not easily understood by the layperson unless constructed with great attention to detail which may be costly. Even then they do not necessarily give a clear idea of what the view will look like from a particular vantage point;

- **Colour photomontage:** has the advantage that it represents the landscape in a form that most people are familiar with. It is relatively easily reproduced, and is not expensive to create. The principal difficulty comes with representing the proposed development which has to be incorporated into, the photograph with accuracy and at an appropriate level of detail.

- **Film and video montage:** provides useful simulations to represent proposed development where movement is a particular feature.

ASSESSMENT OF LANDSCAPE

25. **Scoping:** At the outset of the investigation it is important to establish:

- current landscape designation and policies covering the site and its surroundings;

- whether a landscape assessment has been undertaken of the site and its surroundings by the local authority or other organisation;

- where the potential zone of influence for the development and its associated infrastructure will extend to, based on an initial site visit and reference to OS maps and aerial photographs.

26. In combination, the information should establish the potential landscape key issues and the areas requiring further investigation during the baseline studies.

27. **Baseline Surveys:** the baseline studies may include a landscape assessment where this does not already exist, followed by a visual impact assessment of the development.

28. **Prediction and Significance of Impacts:** Impacts on landscape resources may be assessed in terms of changes in landscape character, and loss of specific elements. Criteria for evaluation include questions of local, regional or national importance, rarity or uniqueness of landscape affected, special association or cultural values, and impact on designated areas.

29. Where appropriate, local, regional and national landscape designations such as National Parks, AONBs and NSAs should be considered in evaluating the importance of change. Other sensitive areas without statutory designation, for example, heritage coasts should also receive consideration.

30. The significance of impacts on the perceived landscape will depend partly on quantification of the number of people who will be affected, but also on judgements about how much the changes will matter to those concerned. In both cases, judgements should, as far as possible, reflect assessments of the attitudes of different groups of people. Wide consultation will greatly assist in providing a balanced and representative view of the proposals.

31. **Mitigation of Impacts and Positive Benefits:** For almost all projects there will be scope to improve the quality of the end result by incorporating measures to ameliorate or mitigate potentially adverse effects. In landscape terms, this can involve screening, on-site and (where practicable) off-site tree planting and modifications to design. It is important that residual impacts which cannot be 'designed-out' are clearly identified in the ES. Mitigation of visual impact can be achieved under the three headings below

32. **Avoidance** involves the elimination of potential visual impacts through the adoption of alternative courses of action. These alternatives may be either in overall site location or location of the development within the selected site, or in the design of the proposal.

33. **Reduction** represents the scope for decreasing the development's exposure to public view. This may be achieved by: careful siting of the development using existing topography and vegetation for concealment; screening the development with new environmental features like walls, earthworks and trees to block or

reduce the line-of-sight to the development; and detailed design of the development in the selection of forms, colours and finishes to minimise the contrasts with the existing environment.

34. **Remedies or Compensation** should be considered in situations where visual impact cannot be avoided, for example, where trees have to be felled or earthworks undertaken to enable the project to proceed. This form of mitigation addresses visual impact by aiming to restore or rehabilitate the landscape to an apparently undisturbed state through earthmodelling or new tree and shrub planting. (See also Appendix 5)

35. Mitigation measures are often undertaken in order to address other impacts of the development. For example, a belt of new planting may provide a reduction in dust and noise emissions generated by the development itself and by roads and car parking within a site, while also effectively screening external views of the new development. But, however good these measures may be, they will seldom achieve their full effect immediately following construction of the project. It may be preferable to begin them, if possible, before the first stages of construction. Landscape assessments should, therefore, predict the timescale for maturity to be reached and describe the intervening conditions and the requirement for continued management of the mitigation measures to ensure they remain effective.

POSITIVE BENEFITS

36. Some developments may have a positive landscape impact, such as by reshaping of reclaiming derelict or unsightly land as part of the project. Such benefits need to be clearly and objectively assessed and presented, and any temporary disbenefits during the development process should be addressed (eg. extra noise of dust from removal of reshaping of old waste tips or derelict structures), and mitigating measures proposed for these impacts. In addition the local community may have become used to particular features which "outsiders" would consider detracted from the landscape. These perceptions should be included in the assessments.

Selected Sources of Further Information

- Countryside Commission (1993) Landscape Assessment Guidance (CCP 423) - Countryside Commission, Cheltenham.

- Countryside Commission (1993) Design in the Countryside (CCP 418) - Countryside Commission, Cheltenham

- Guidelines for Landscape and Visual Impact Assessment (1995) - published jointly by the Landscape Institute and the Institute of Environmental Assessment.

- Landscape Assessment: Principles and Practice (1992), a report prepared for the Countryside Commission for Scotland (now known as Scottish Natural Heritage).

- National Rivers Authority (1993) - River Landscape Assessment, Conservation Technical Handbook 2 - National Rivers Authority, Bristol

CULTURAL HERITAGE/MATERIAL ASSETS

1. 'Cultural Heritage' is the collective term used to describe aspects of the environment which reflect the history of human activities, ideas and attitudes. It is not limited to material and economic aspects of life, but also reflects spiritual and intellectual value. The term embraces the subject areas of history, archaeology, architecture and urban design, and in many cases is closely tied to the rural or urban landscape. For the purpose of this Guide, 'cultural heritage' and 'material assets' are treated as a single topic area.

2. It is important that cultural heritage is adequately covered during an EA, since it is generally irreplaceable and should be viewed in the same light as other finite or non-renewable resources.

EXISTING INFORMATION AND LEGISLATION

Archaeology

3. Although archaeological remains are a fundamental part of our heritage, development and other human activities continue to result in damage or loss of archaeological sites. It is essential therefore that any archaeological remains, which may not be visible, should be identified before development on a given site takes place. For England and Wales, PPG 16 - Archaeology and Planning[1], gives advice on handling archaeological remains and other discoveries under planning procedures. It stresses the importance of early consultations between local authorities, archaeologists and developers, and places the onus on local authorities, through their development plan policies, to promote the protection, enhancement and preservation of sites of archaeological interest, and on developers to fund appropriate archaeological works prior to development. Where nationally important archaeological remains, (whether scheduled or not) and their settings are affected by proposed development there is a presumption in favour of their physical preservation.

4. The National Monuments Record held by the Royal Commission on the Historical Monuments of England provides a national overview of records available for the cultural heritage, both archaeology and buildings, and includes the National

[1] In Scotland NPPG 5 (Archaeology and Planning) and Planning Advice Note 42 (Archaeology) apply

Archaeological record of sites and monuments in England and the national library of air photographs. Similar information can be obtained from the Royal Commissions on Ancient and Historical Monuments of Scotland and of Wales. The National Records and local 'Sites and Monuments Records' (SMRs), usually held by county councils in England, by 4 regional archaeological trusts in Wales, and in Scotland by regional and island councils, should provide a catalogue of known archaeological sites. The records are continually being updated as significant new sites are identified and some are given statutory protection as 'Scheduled Monuments' under the Ancient Monuments and Archaeological Areas Act 1979. Local authorities may also designate their own policy areas, such as 'Areas of Archaeological Significance', in development plans.

5. The national importance of a monument and the appropriateness of scheduling is assessed according to eight criteria, although selection is also designed to ensure a representative sample of each 'class' of monument. These criteria provide a useful framework within which to judge both nationally important and locally important archaeological remains. They are period, rarity, documentation, group value (importance may be enhanced by association with other monuments), survival and condition, fragility or vulnerability, diversity and potential (where the importance of remains cannot be precisely known but there is good evidence to anticipate it).

6. Designations provide a useful, but not exhaustive schedule of sites. Some sites are outside the scope of current legislation and many await the completion of the Monuments Protection Programme. The absence of scheduled sites from an area must not be taken as evidence that it is devoid of sites or landscapes of archaeological importance. In addition, sites and landscapes of more regional or local importance have a contribution to make. In some cases they will contribute to the local distinctiveness of an area. Early consultation with the county archaeologists or English Heritage in England, the Archaeological Trust or Cadw in Wales, and the Regional/Islands Archaeologist or Historic Scotland in Scotland should help identify the cultural importance of the site or area.

Maritime Archaeology

7. The 'cultural heritage' is not confined to land. Historic shipwrecks may be designated under the Protection of Wrecks Act 1973. Any survey, excavation or development proposals affecting such sites may be subject to the granting of a licence for that purpose from the Secretary of State for National Heritage or the Secretaries of State for Scotland and Wales. While development below the low watermark is not generally subject to planning control, the consent of the relevant Government Department may be required and EA may be required as part of the consent procedure, as, for example, with applications for licences to extract marine minerals. It may also be the case that a development on land may have an impact on underwater sites, which would need to be taken into account when assessing an EA. The Royal Commissions listed in paragraph 4 should be consulted on

the archaeological potential of the proposed area of development.

WORLD HERITAGE SITES

8. There are at present 10 World Heritage Sites in England and 4 in Wales. No additional statutory controls follow from the inclusion of sites in he UNESCO World Heritage List, but inclusion does highlight the outstanding international importance of the sites as a key material consideration to be taken into account. Information about World Heritage Sites in England is given in PPG 15.

Historic Buildings

9. Buildings of special architectural or historic interest make an important contribution to the quality and character of the built environment. Under the Planning (Listed Buildings and Conservation Areas) Act 1990 the most important historic buildings in England and Wales are 'listed' and are afforded statutory protection.

10. Listed buildings in England and Wales[2] are classified in 3 grades to show relative importance: Grade I (only about 2% of listed buildings are in this category); Grade II* (some 4% of listed buildings); and Grade II.

    The current principles for selecting buildings to be listed are:

    - All buildings built before 1700 which survive in anything like their original condition;
    - Most buildings built between 1700-1840, though selection is necessary;
    - Buildings constructed between 1840-1914.
    - Only selected buildings from the period after 1914 are listed;
    - Buildings which are less than 30 years old are normally only listed if they are of outstanding quality. Buildings which are less than 10 years old are not listed.

11. The following are the main criteria which the Secretary of State applies in deciding which buildings to include in the statutory lists:

    - **architectural interest:** the lists are meant to include all buildings which are of importance to the nation for the interest of their architectural design, decoration and craftsmanship; also important examples of particular building types and techniques, eg buildings displaying technological innovation or virtuosity, and significant plan forms;

[2] In Scotland buildings of special architectural or historical interest are listed under the Town and Country Planning (Scotland) Act 1972. The criteria for selection and listing are different to those set out in paragraphs 9 and 10. For details of the criteria which apply in Scotland please contact Historic Scotland, Longmore House, Salisbury Place , Edinburgh, EH9 1FH.

- **historic interest:** this includes buildings which illustrate important aspects of the nation's social, economic, cultural or military history;

- **close historical associations** with nationally important people or events;

- **group value,** especially where buildings comprise together an important architectural or historical unity or a fine example of planning, eg squares, terraces or model villages.

A particular building may qualify for listing under more than one of these criteria.

Conservation Areas

12. Areas of special architectural or historical interest, the character or appearance of which it is desirable to preserve or enhance, may be designated as Conservation Areas. This designation recognises the importance of securing the protection of groupings of buildings. Conservation Areas may be centred on listed buildings and may also include pleasant groups of other buildings, open spaces, trees, an historic street pattern, a village green or features of historic or archaeological interest. These should all contribute to the special character of an area.

13. In addition to listed buildings and Conservation Areas there are many more buildings and settlements which, while unprotected, are also valuable contributors to the rural and urban scene. Consideration should be given to the contribution these may make to the character, appearance, fabric, and archaeological, historic or architectural integrity of an area in and around a proposed development site.

Historic Landscapes

14. Historic landscapes are also an integral part of cultural heritage and are an increasingly scarce and threatened resource. Historic landscapes may be valued as:

- works of art in their own right, based on their aesthetic quality;

- providing a significant historical record;

- providing a setting for buildings or monuments of architectural or archaeological importance;

- making a particular contribution to the variety of scenery in the countryside;

- containing valued habitats for wildlife.

They may occur in an industrial, urban or rural location.

15. Historic landscapes may be afforded special protection as part of a larger designated landscape (such as a National Park or AONB), but, unlike scheduled ancient monuments and listed buildings, are not currently provided with statutory protection. Nevertheless, they make an important contribution to the character of the landscape generally in conjunction with many factors including archaeological features and historic buildings. Other landscape resources are mentioned in Appendix 9.

Parks and Gardens

16. English Heritage maintain the Register of Parks and Gardens of special historic interest in England. It is published in a set of County Volumes. Local authorities should have copies of the volumes of the Register relating to their areas. Sites of exceptional historic interest are assessed as Grade I, those of great historic interest as Grade II*, and those of special historic interest as Grade II. (The grading of these sites is independent of the grading of any listed building which falls within the area.) Inclusion on the register is a material consideration when planning permission is sought for development that would affect the character of a registered park or garden. In Scotland the Inventory of Gardens and Designed Landscapes is maintained by Scottish Natural Heritage and copies are held by planning authorities. The Secretary of State has to be consulted when they may be affected by a development proposal.

17. In Wales, Cadw, (Welsh Historic Monuments Executive Agency) is preparing a register of Historic Parks and Gardens in the principality which is expected to be completed by the end of 1996.

Historic Battlefields

18. English Heritage introduced a Register of Historic Battlefields in England in 1995 which identifies a limited number of areas of historic significance where important battles are sufficiently documented to be located on the ground. They are not graded. Further information may be obtained from English Heritage. In Scotland, details of historic battlefield sites are kept by Historic Scotland.

POTENTIAL IMPACTS

19. Developments of many different types and in many different locations have the potential to cause direct and indirect impacts on cultural heritage. These are often likely to be negative unless attention has been given to them during the design process. The following summary is not intended to be exhaustive, but merely to illustrate the range of potential impacts. It should be clear from these that the impacts can be complex and need not be direct. Further guidance of the position in England is given in PPG15 - Planning and the Historic Environment. In Scotland information is available in the Memorandum of Guidance on Listed Buildings and of Conservation Areas published by Historic Scotland, in NPPG 5 and in PAN 42.

20. **Loss/Destruction:** The most dramatic potential negative impact is the direct loss or destruction of an element of cultural heritage. This, for example, may include the demolition of an historic building or the disturbance of an archaeological feature during the construction of a development.

21. **Visual Intrusion:** This is a potentially important impact in both urban and rural settings. An unsympathetic development may impinge on the character and appearance of an area through inappropriate siting or design - directly affecting Conservation Areas, historic buildings, ancient monuments, areas of archaeological importance, historic landscapes and settlements.

22. **Physical Damage:** There are a number of impacts which may potentially cause damage to the physical fabric of archaeological remains, historic buildings or historic landscapes. These include:

    - **air pollution:** which may cause damage to historic buildings and ancient monuments;

    - **water;** water table fluctuations may affect archaeological remains otherwise preserved by water-logging;

    - **vibration:** which may cause damage to historic buildings, ancient monuments and archaeological remains. This may be a potential impact during construction, or during the operation of certain developments;

    - **recreation pressure:** which may occur as a result of improved access or by directly attracting visitors. This may cause physical damage and change the intrinsic character of the feature;

    - **ecological damage:** there are a number of potential impacts which may affect flora and fauna as a result of a particular development. These impacts may also affect cultural heritage, as flora and fauna is an important component of heritage features, particularly historic landscapes. Potential impacts outlined in Appendix 5 on flora and fauna may therefore be relevant to cultural heritage.

ASSESSMENT OF EFFECTS ON CULTURAL HERITAGE

23. **Scoping:** At the outset it is important to establish the potential value of the development site with regard to the three main components of cultural heritage: namely below ground archaeology, historic buildings and historic landscapes, and their inter-relationships. Where the site is well documented or contains listed structures or features, this importance can usually be established quickly. However, lack of information does not mean that a site is devoid of interest; it may yet require investigation, especially with regard to archaeology and historic landscape features. In these instances, a site visit, combined with discussions with appropriate individuals or organisations, should help clarify the position.

24. The scoping phase should end with identification of any requirements for further information to be collected during the baseline studies. These should focus on the potential types of impact which the development could have at any phase, and the potential cultural value of the site.

25. **Baseline Surveys:** Any further baseline studies should be undertaken by those with expertise in the area of cultural heritage. Additional work required to describe the existing situation may consist of :

- archive research, including study of aerial photographs, old maps, paintings and literary references illustrating the site's history;
- field study by a trained archaeologist and geophysical surveys where appropriate;
- trial excavations by a trained archaeologist.

26. **Prediction of Impacts:** Like the baseline studies, the prediction of impacts and an evaluation of their significance will need to be undertaken by an expert in cultural heritage. During this assessment it will be important to consider not only direct impacts such as loss or damage of important features but also indirect impacts such as changing water table levels which can affect the preservation of archaeological or designed landscape features in situ.

27. **Mitigation of Impacts:** By adopting good practice and certain mitigation measures it may be possible to address many of the potential impacts of a development on cultural heritage. The primary method of mitigating adverse impacts is to recognise the site or monument early in the planning and site selection process and avoid it (preservation in situ), leaving a suitable buffer zone round the site. In the case of nationally important monuments, buildings and landscapes there should be a general presumption in favour of their preservation unless it can be shown that the need for a particular development in a sensitive location is unavoidable and outweighs the significance of the heritage feature.

28. If avoidance is not a possible alternative, amelioration can be achieved by reduction of the potential impacts and the preservation of heritage features, which could involve physically relocating a monument. In the case of visual intrusion affecting the character of cultural heritage, reduction of the degree of exposure of the development can be achieved by siting, screening and detailed design.

29. In the case of archaeological remains where destruction is unavoidable, appropriate provisions may be necessary to excavate and record remains before development commences (rescue excavation), depending on the merits of individual sites. In urban situations where archaeological remains are in deep stratified layers spanning centuries of occupation, construction design sympathetic to the preservation of archaeological deposits in situ may be required. If the site is 'unpredictable' in its

archaeological potential, it may be necessary to arrange for the construction stage to be overseen by an archaeologist and for the provision to be made for adequate recording of archaeological features so identified.

30. The need to reconcile archaeology and development and to avoid potential conflicts has led to the production of two codes of practice for land based archaeology produced by the British Archaeologists and Developers Liaison Group and the Confederation of British Industry (specifically for mineral operators). For developments below the low water mark, the Crown Estate Commissioners have published the Joint Nautical Archaeology Policy Committee Code of Practice for Seabed Developers this year. If these codes are followed, along with the guidance in PPG 16, conflicts and impacts can be largely mitigated.

Selected Sources of Further Information

- Joint Nautical Archaeology Policy Committee Code of Practice for Seabed Developers - Crown Estate Commissioners (1995)
- National Planning Policy Guidelines 5 - Archaeology and Planning - Scottish Office
- Planning Advice Note 42 - Archaeology - Scottish Office
- Planning Policy Guidance Note 15 - Planning and the Historic Environment - Department of the Environment/ Department of National Heritage (1994)
- Planning Policy Guidance Note 16 - Archaeology and Planning -Department of the Environment (1990)
- Planning Policy Guidance Note 16 (Wales) - Archaeology and Planning - Welsh Office

ABBREVIATIONS

AONB	Area of Outstanding Natural Beauty
DOE	Department of the Environment
EA	Environmental Assessment (aka EIA, Environmental Impact Assessment)
EC	European Commission
ES	Environmental Statement
HMIP	Her Majesty's Inspectorate of Pollution[1]
HMIPI	Her Majesty's Industrial Pollution Inspectorate[1]
HMSO	Her Majesty's Stationery Office (Tel Orders 0171-873-9090)
IPC	Integrated Pollution Control
MAFF	Ministry of Agriculture, Fisheries and Food
NCC	Nature Conservancy Council
NPPG	National Planning Policy Guidelines
NRA	National Rivers Authority[1]
OS	Ordnance Survey
PAN	Planning Advice Note
PPG	Planning Policy Guidance
RIGS	Regionally Important Geological Site
RQO	River Quality Objectives
SO	Scottish Office
SSSI	Site of Special Scientific Interest
WO	Welsh Office

[1] As from 1st April 1996, in England and Wales the Environment Agency will take over the functions of the National Rivers Authority and Her Majesty's Inspectorate of Pollution and in Scotland the Scottish Environment Protection Agency will take over the functions of the River Purification Authorities and Her Majesty's Industrial Pollution Inspectorate.

GLOSSARY

Baseline studies	Studies of existing environmental conditions which are designed to establish the baseline conditions against which any future changes can be measured or predicted.
"Do-nothing" scenario	The predicted future environmental conditions which would exist in the absence of the development.
Ecosystem	A community of interdependent plants and animals together with the environment which they inhabit and with which they interact.
EA Planning Regulations	In England and Wales they are The Town and Country Planning (Assessment of Environmental Effects) Regulations 1988, plus amendments. In Scotland they are the Environmental Assessment (Scotland) Regulations 1988, plus amendments. A full list of EA legislation is given in Annex I.
EIA Directive	Directive 85/337/EEC on the assessment of the effects of certain public and private projects on the environment. Reproduced in the Guide to Procedures.
Environmental Assessment	A process by which information about the environmental effects of a project is collected, both by the developer and from other sources, and taken into account by the relevant decision making body before a decision is given on whether the development should go ahead. Note: In this Guide, EA is used to refer to that part of the process whereby the developer collects information about the environmental effects of a project for assembly in an environmental statement.
Environmental Effects	The consequences for human being in terms of health and well-being, including the well-being of ecosystems and natural systems on which human survival depends, which stem from environmental impacts.
Environmental Impacts	The processes whereby a change, which may be adverse, beneficial, or both, is brought about in the existing environment as a result of development activities.

Environmental Statement	A document which sets out the developer's assessment of the likely effects of the project on the environment and which is submitted in conjunction with an application for planning permission.
Fauna	All members of the animal kingdom: vertebrates (eg birds, mammals and fish) and invertebrates (eg insects).
Flora	All members of the plant kingdom : higher ferns, ferns and fern allies, mosses and liverworts, algae and phytoplankton, fungi and lichens.
Guide to Procedures	The DOE book "Environmental Assessment : A Guide to the Procedures". Published by HMSO, ISBN 0-11-752244-9
Mitigation	Any process, activity or thing designed to avoid, reduce or remedy adverse environmental impacts likely to be caused by a development project.
Pathways	The routes by which impacts are transmitted through air, water, soils or plants and organisms to their receptors.
Potential impacts	Impacts which could occur in the absence of appropriate design modifications or preventative measures.
Predicted impacts	Those impacts which are predicted as a consequence of the development although the nature and severity of their effect will be conditioned by the scope for mitigation.
Receptors	A component of the natural or man made environment such as water, air, a building, or a plant that is affected by an impact.
Scoping	An initial stage in determining the nature and potential scale of the environmental impacts arising from the proposed development, and assessing what further studies are required to establish their significance.

ENVIRONMENTAL ASSESSMENT: STATUTORY INSTRUMENTS AND OTHER DOCUMENTS

Council Directive 85/337/EEC of 27 June 1985 on the assessment of the effects of certain public and private projects on the environment (the EIA Directive) is printed in the Official Journal of the European Communities, page No. L 175/40 dated 5.7.85 and Appendix 7 of the "Guide to the Procedures."

The following Regulations implementing the EIA Directive in the United Kingdom and Gibraltar have been made:

i. Town and Country Planning (Assessment of Environmental Effects) Regulations 1988 (Statutory Instrument No 1199)

ii. Environmental Assessment (Scotland) Regulations 1988 (Statutory Instrument No 1221)

iii. Environmental Assessment (Salmon Farming in Marine Waters) Regulations 1988 (Statutory Instrument No 1218)

iv. Environmental Assessment (Afforestation) Regulations 1988 (Statutory Instrument No 1207)

v. Land Drainage Improvement Works (Assessment of Environmental Effects) Regulations 1988 (Statutory Instrument No 1217)

vi. Highways (Assessment of Environmental Effects) Regulations 1988 (Statutory Instrument No 1241)

vii. Harbour Works (Assessment of Environmental Effects) Regulations 1988 (Statutory Instrument No 1336)

viii. Town and Country Planning General Development (Amendment) Order 1988 (Statutory Instrument No 1272). Note: revoked by Statutory Instrument 1988 No 1813 (General Development Order 1988). The 1988 Order has been replaced by The Town and Country Planning (General Permitted Development)

Order 1995 (Statutory Instrument No 418) and The Town and Country Planning (General Development Procedure) Order 1995 (Statutory Instrument No 419)

ix. Town and Country Planning (General Development) (Scotland) Amendment Order 1988 (Statutory Instrument No 977)

x. Town and Country Planning (General Development) (Scotland) Amendment No 2 Order 1988 (Statutory Instrument No 1249). Note: revoked by Statutory Instrument 1992 No 224 (see item xxiv below)

xi. Electricity and Pipe-line Works (Assessment of Environmental Effects) Regulations 1989 (Statutory Instrument No 167) Note: revoked by Statutory Instrument 1990 No 442 (See item xiv below)

xii. Harbour Works (Assessment of Environmental Effects) (No 2) Regulations 1989 (Statutory Instrument No 424)

xiii. Town and Country Planning (Assessment of Environmental Effects) (Amendment) Regulations 1990 (Statutory Instrument No 367)

xiv. Electricity and Pipe-line Works (Assessment of Environmental Effects) Regulations 1990 (Statutory Instrument No 442) (Note: revoked Statutory Instrument 167 1989)

xv. Roads (Assessment of Environmental Effects) Regulations (Northern Ireland) 1988 (Statutory Rule No 344). Note: revoked by Statutory Rule No 3160 (NI 15) (see item xxv below)

xvi. Planning (Assessment of Environmental Effects) Regulations (Northern Ireland 1989 (Statutory Rule No 20)

xvii. Environmental Assessment (Afforestation) Regulations (Northern Ireland) 1989 (Statutory Rule No. 226)

xviii. Harbour Works (Assessment of Environmental Effects) Regulations (Northern Ireland) 1990 (Statutory Rule No 181)

xix. Drainage (Environmental Assessment) Regulations (Northern Ireland) 1991 (Statutory Rule No. 376)

xx. Town and Country Planning (Assessment of Environmental Effects) (Amendment) Regulations 1992 (Statutory Instrument No 1494)

xxi. Harbour Works (Assessment of Environmental Effects) Regulations 1992 (Statutory Instrument No 1421)

xxii. Town and Country Planning (Simplified Planning Zones) Regulations 1992 (Statutory Instrument No 2414) (Regulation 22)

xxiii. Transport and Works (Application and Objections Procedure) Rules 1992 (Statutory Instrument No 2902)

xxiv. Town and Country Planning (General Development Procedure) (Scotland) Order 1992 (Statutory Instrument No 224) (Article 16)

xxv. Roads (Northern Ireland) Order 1993 (Statutory Rule No 3160 (NI 15)) (Article 67). Note: revokes Statutory Rule No 344 (see item xv above)

xxvi. Planning (Simplified Planning Zones) (Excluded Development) Order (Northern Ireland) 1994 (Statutory Rule 1994 No 426)

xxvii. Town and Country Planning (Assessment of Environmental Effects) (Amendment) Regulations 1994 (Statutory Instrument No 677)

xxviii. Town and Country Planning General Development (Amendment) Order 1994 (Statutory Instrument No 678)

xxix. Highways (Assessment of Environmental Effects) Regulations 1994 (Statutory Instrument No 1002)

xxx. Environmental Assessment (Scotland) Amendment Regulations 1994 (Statutory Instrument No 2012 (S.91))

xxxi. Roads (Assessment of Environmental Effects) Regulations (Northern Ireland) 1994 (Statutory Rule No 316)

xxxii. Planning (Assessment of Environmental Effects) (Amendment) Regulations (Northern Ireland) 1994 (Statutory Rule 395)

xxxiii. The Town and Country Planning (Environmental Assessment and Permitted Development) Regulations 1995 (Statutory Instrument 417)

xxxiv. The Town and Country Planning (General Permitted Development) Order 1995 (Statutory Instrument No 418) [NOTE: Article 3 introduces EA for otherwise Permitted Development]

xxxv. The Town and Country Planning (General Development Procedure) Order 1995 (Statutory Instrument No 419) [NOTE: replaces 1988 Order in respect of Article 14]

xxxvi. The Town Planning (Applications) (Amendment) Regulations 1993 Made Pursuant to the Town Planning Ordinance. [Regulations for Gibraltar] xxxvii. The Transport and Works (Assessment of Environmental Effects) Regulations 1995 (Statutory Instruments No 1541) (Amends Statutory Instrument 1992 No 2902)

xxxviii. The Land Drainage Improvement Works (Assessment of Environmental Effects) (Amendment) Regulations 1995 (Statutory Instrument No 2195)

xxxix. The Town and Country Planning (Environmental Assessment and Unauthorised Development) Regulations 1995 (Statutory Instrument No 2258)

GUIDANCE

i. Department of the Environment Circular 15/88 (Welsh Office 23/88) "Environmental Assessment" dated 12 July 1988

ii. Scottish Development Department Circular 13/88 "Environmental Assessment Implementation of European Commission Directive: The Environmental Assessment (Scotland) Regulations 1988" dated 12 July 1988

iii. Department of the Environment (Northern Ireland) Development Control Advice Note No 10 - "Environmental Impact Assessment", published 1989

iv. "Environmental Assessment of Marine Salmon Farms" note by Crown Estate Office dated 15 July 1988

v. Department of the Environment Circular 24/88 (Welsh Office 48/88) "Environmental Assessment of Projects in Simplified Planning Zones and Enterprise Zones" dated 25 November 1988. Note: cancelled insofar as it relates to Special Planning Zones by Statutory Instrument 1992 No 2414

vi. Scottish Development Department Circular 26/88 "Environmental Assessment of Projects in Simplified Planning Zones and Enterprise Zones" (relates to Scotland) dated 25 November 1988

vii. Department of the Environment Memorandum of 30 March 1989 to the General Managers of New Towns Development Corporations and to the Chief Executive of the Commission for the New Towns on "Environmental Assessment" (advice on projects arising in new towns)

viii. Department of Transport and Planning Departmental Standard notice HD18/88 "Environmental Assessment under European Commission Directive 85/337 "A Guide To Procedures" dated July 1989 (Note : WITHDRAWN - Replaced by Vol 11, Department of Transport Design Manual.)

ix. Department of the Environment/Welsh Office advisory booklet "Environmental Assessment: A Guide to the Procedures", published 1989. ISBN 0-11-752244-9

x. Department of the Environment free leaflet "Environmental Assessment"

xi. Welsh Office free leaflet "Environmental Assessment/Assu'r Amgylchedd" (bilingual)

xii. Scottish Office free leaflet "Environmental Assessment - a Guide"

xiii. Overseas Development Administration "Manual Of Environmental Appraisal", revised April 1992

xiv. Department of the Environment Circular 15/92 (Welsh Office 32/92) "Publicity for Planning Applications" dated 3 June 1992 (paras 15-16)

xv. Department of the Environment Circular 19/92 (Welsh Office 39/92) "The Town and Country Planning General Regulations 1992/The Town and Country Planning (Development Plans and Consultation) Directions 1992" dated 13 July 1992 (paras 36-40)

xvi. Department of Transport guide "Transport and Works Act 1992: a Guide to Procedures for obtaining orders relating to transport systems, inland waterways and works interfering with rights of navigation" published 1992

xvii. Department of the Environment Policy Planning Guidance Note 5 "Simplified Planning Zones" dated November 1992 (paras 7-9 of Annex A and Appendices 1 & 2)

xviii. Department of Trade and Industry booklet "Guidance on Environmental Assessment of Cross- Country Pipelines" published 1992

xix. Forestry Commission booklet "Environmental Assessment of New Woodlands" dated April 1993 (replaces Forestry Commission booklet "Environmental Assessment of Afforestation" dated 4 August 1988)

xx. Vol. 11 "Environmental Assessment", the Design Manual for Roads and Bridges, produced by Department of Transport/Scottish Office Industry Department/The Welsh Office and Department of the Environment for Northern Ireland, dated June 1993

xxi. Department of the Environment Circular 7/94 (Welsh Office 20/94) "Environmental Assessment: Amendment of Regulations" dated 18 March 1994

xxii. Scottish Office Environment Department Circular 26/94 "The Environmental Assessment (Scotland) Amendment Regulations 1994"

xxiii. Department of the Environment Circular 3/95 (Welsh Office 12/95) "Permitted Development and Environmental Assessment"

xxiv. Department of the Environment and Welsh Office Booklet "Your Permitted Development Rights and Environmental Assessment" March 1995

xxv. Department of the Environment Circular 11/95 "The Use of Conditions in Planning Permissions" Paragraph 77 - Use of conditions to enforce mitigation measures

xxvi. Department of the Environment Circular 13/95 (Welsh Office 39/95) "The Town and Country Planning (Environmental Assessment and Unauthorised Development) Regulations 1995

The following documents do not necessarily represent the views of the Department of the Environment, the Scottish Office Environment Department or the Welsh Office; the findings and conclusions within them are those of the authors.

i. "Monitoring Environmental Assessment and Planning" (1991). A report by the Environment Impact Assessment Centre Manchester. HMSO, London. ISBN 0-11-752436-0

ii. "Evaluation of Environmental information for Planning Projects: A Good Practice Guide" (1994). A report by Land Use Consultants. HMSO, London. ISBN 0-11-753043-3

iii. "Good Practice on the Evaluation of Environmental Information for Planning Projects: Research Report" (1994). A report by Land Use Consultants assisted by the University of East Anglia. HMSO, London. ISBN 0-11-752990-7

Designed by DDP Services
B1704, 11/95

Printed in the United Kingdom for HMSO
Dd 0301734 C11 12/95 65536 3400/4 339129 46/34083